CONTENTS

ABOUT THIS BOOK

This is a revision book, not a text book. It will show you everything you need to know in the Math Studies syllabus, but it assumes that you have already covered the work, and that you are now going through it for the second (or third, or fourth ....) time. I would expect you to use your other resources (text book, class notes) to fill in much of the detail.

The exam is not so much a test of your knowledge and understanding (you will not get a question which begins "What do you know about ....?"); but a test of how you use your understanding to solve mathematical problems. So the emphasis in this revision book is on how to answer questions. In particular you will find plenty of worked exam style questions, as well as further ones for *you* to solve. All the questions in boxes are of a standard and of a type that could occur in your exams. Do not skim over these – much useful revision material is contained in the working which is not contained in the text.

You are expected to be able to understand and use your graphic display calculator (GDC) in many areas of the syllabus. Indeed, some questions *require* you to use, for example, the graphing or the equation solving features. Since different people use different calculators, it is not possible for this book to explain the detail of their use; but I have indicated (using the calculator symbol ▪) where the GDC can be particularly useful. If you have a calculator from the TI-83 family, you might like to know that another book in the OSC Revision Guide series, "Using the TI-83 calculator in IB Maths", will guide you through all the techniques you need.

This is *your* revision book. Every page has a wide column for you to make notes and scribblings and write down questions to ask your teacher; and there are plenty of questions for *you* to work through.

> **"You Solve" questions appear in boxes like this with a grey indicator bar at the side.**

And on the next page there are some important points about how to maximise your exam mark. *Do* follow the suggestions there, and perhaps add some more of your own.

At the very end there are some practice questions testing you on the basic work contained in each area of the syllabus.

I am hugely grateful to Chris Reisemann who has spent much of his summer holiday proof-reading this book. It takes a truly dedicated mathematician to admit that his favourite activity on the beach is working through mathematics problems! Nonetheless, in spite of his meticulous attention to detail, the responsibility for any remaining errors is wholly mine: should you come across any, please let me know and I will correct them for future editions.

Through Oxford Study Courses I have been privileged to help many students revise towards their IB Mathematics exams, and much of what I have learnt from teaching them has been distilled into this book. I would value any feedback so that later editions can continue to help students around the world. Please feel free to e-mail me on inlucas@greentrees.fsnet.co.uk. All correspondence will be answered personally.

Ian Lucas

MAXIMISING YOUR MARKS

Remember that the examiner is on your side – he *wants* to give you marks! Make it easy for him to find them, even if you are not quite sure what you are doing or if you are getting wrong answers. You cannot *lose* marks for doing things wrong. LEARN THIS CHECKLIST.

Before you start a question:
- Read it carefully so you know what it is about.
- Highlight important words.

Answering a question:
- Check any calculations you do, preferably using a different method or order of operation.
- Show your working – there are often marks for method as well as for the right answer. And, in a longer question, a wrong answer at the start may mean lots more wrong answers – but the examiner will probably give you marks for correct methods, and will check your working against your original answer.
- Make sure you have answered *exactly* what the question asked. For example, have you been asked to calculate the new value of an investment or the amount of interest earned.
- In longer questions, don't worry if you can't work out the answer to a part. Carry on with the rest, using their answer (if one is given) or even making up a reasonable answer.
- Don't spend too long on any question or part of a question – you may lose the opportunity to answer easier questions later on. You can always come back and fill in gaps.
- The algebra can be tough – keep going!
- Check the units in questions – are they mixed?

The "golden three":
- WHAT are you working out?
- HOW are you going to work it out?
- WHAT is the answer?

eg: Where do the lines
$y = x + 3$ and $x + 2y = 0$
intersect?

Lines intersect when $y = -2y + 3$
$$3y = 3$$
$$y = 1$$
Point of intersection = $(-2, 1)$

| WHAT | HOW | ANSWER |

Diagrams:
- Do not assume facts from diagrams, especially if they are marked NOT TO SCALE. For example, it may *look* like a right angle but does the question *tell* you that it is. Two lines may *look* parallel but they aren't unless you are *told* they are.
- And do draw your own diagrams – not necessarily to hand in as part of the question, but to help you sort out what's going on.

Key words in questions:
- STATE – put the answer down without working (should be an easy one)!
- WRITE DOWN – minimal working required.
- SHOW – show enough working to get to the given answer.
- EVALUATE – give a value to, work out.
- SKETCH A GRAPH – draw its shape and show key points (eg: where it cuts the axes)
- PLOT A GRAPH – work out points and draw the graph accurately
- EXACT VALUE – not a rounded decimal eg: 2π, not 6.28...

SHOW $x = 3$ is the solution of
$2x + 1 = 7$.
$$2 \times 3 + 1 = 7$$
(We have not had to *solve* the equation)

When you have answered the question:
- Check you have answered every part of the question.
- Check you have answered exactly what was asked.
- Check you have answered to the correct accuracy (normally 3 SF)
- Check that what you have written is clear, and that your answer is not mixed up in the working somewhere.

DO THESE CHECKS – you will probably pick up a few marks.

NUMBER AND ALGEBRA
Number Systems and Accuracy

Different situations require different types of number. For example, populations of countries will always be given as positive, whole numbers, whereas the division of a reward will require the use of fractions. These are known as *number systems*, and the ones you need to know are:

Symbols:
Naturals   N
Integers   Z
Rationals   Θ
Irrationals I
Reals   P

Natural numbers – positive whole numbers
Integers – whole numbers including negatives and zero
Rationals – numbers which can be written as fractions in their simplest form
Irrationals – numbers which can't be written as fractions
Reals – the rationals and the irrationals put together. The reals will include every possible number you could meet in the course.

Decimals do not seem to feature in the list above – are they rational or irrational?

Recurring decimals can always be written as fractions so they are rational numbers.
Terminating decimals can also be written as fractions, so they are rational numbers too.
Non-recurring, non-terminating decimals (ie they carry on for ever and never repeat) can never be written as an exact fraction, so they are irrational numbers.

Exact values: $\sqrt{4} = 2$ since 4 is a square number. However, $\sqrt{10}$ cannot be written exactly – nor can the majority of square roots. It is 3.16228... (the dots indicate that the decimal places will continue for ever without recurring). To 4 significant figures, $\sqrt{10}$ is 3.162, but what do you do if the question asks for an *exact* value? The answer is to use the square root notation:

To be strictly accurate, $x = \pm\sqrt{10}$

$$x^2 = 10 \Rightarrow x = \sqrt{10}$$

and this is the only exact way to write down the solution. And, especially if this is an intermediate answer to a question, it is often better for calculation purposes.

eg: Find the lengths *a* and *b*.

$a^2 = 9^2 + 4^2 = 97 \Rightarrow a = \sqrt{97}$
$b^2 = a^2 - 5^2 = 97 - 25 = 72$

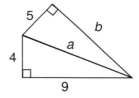

So $b = \sqrt{72}$. The calculation would have been longer (and possibly less accurate) if we had worked out $\sqrt{97}$ as a decimal and used that.

Accuracy: When answering questions which have numerical solutions, it is important to understand how to round numbers to an appropriate level of accuracy. If there are 6 people in a room, then 6 is perfectly accurate. However, a length given as 6cm implies that it lies between 5.5cm and 6.5cm. Strictly, the 6.5 would actually be rounded to 7, so we could say: $5.5 \leq 6 < 6.5$
Note that the number 6.0 implies a greater accuracy:
$$5.95 \leq 6.0 < 6.05$$

You should not give *all* the figures on your calculator because it is possible to be *too* accurate. Consider the following: what is the area of a rectangle with dimensions 4.2cm by 3.8cm? Because the dimensions cannot be accurate (no measurement ever is) the numbers 4.2 and 3.8 represent the ranges shown in the diagram. So the *least* possible value of the area is 4.15 × 3.75 = 15.5625 and the *greatest* value of the area is 4.25 × 3.85 = 16.3625. In other words:

$$15.5625 \le area < 16.3625$$

If we had worked out the area as 4.2 × 3.8 = 15.96cm^2 this just would not be true − it is too accurate. In general, answers should not contain more figures of accuracy than the original numbers − in this case, we would say that area ≈ 16cm^2. As a *general* rule, you can't go too far wrong if you give answers to 3 significant figures.

Significant figures and decimal places: Consider the number 4127. Altering the 4 to a 5 has much more effect on the number than altering the 7 to an 8 − we say that the 4 (ie the number of thousands) is the *most significant* digit. The first significant figure is the first non-zero digit, and the digits which follow (including zeroes) are the 2nd, 3rd, 4th significant figures, and so on. When rounding to, say, 3 significant figures (shortened to S.F.) we write down the first three significant digits, rounding the 3rd up if the 4th is at least 5. It may be necessary to fill spaces with zeroes.

Examples of rounding to 3 S.F:
        16.836 ≈ 16.8
        251.93 ≈ 252
        0.01315 ≈ 0.0132
        23465 ≈ 23500
        12.961 ≈ 13.0 *(The 0 here is significant)*

Note that the decimal point has no effect on the rounding process. However, when rounding to, say, 3 decimal places (D.P.) we simply count up the figures after the decimal point − and then round in exactly the same way.

Examples of rounding to 2 D.P:
        2.1445 ≈ 2.14
        131.131 ≈ 131.13
        0.0291 ≈ 0.03
        1.2951 ≈ 1.30

Rounding errors: In some questions, you may have to do several calculations to get to the answer. You should try and keep all the figures on your calculator as you work and only round the *final* answer to the required accuracy. Otherwise, rounding errors will accumulate and your answer could be some way out. This is especially true when powers are involved. Work out √15 on your calculator, then raise it to the power 5. If you were to round √15 to 3.9, and then raise it to the power 5, just see the difference it makes to the answer!

Percentage error: No measurements are completely accurate; it is important to know how significant any errors are. The best way to express errors is as a percentage of the measurement. For example, I can measure a line to the nearest 0.5cm – what is the percentage error when measuring a line which is 14cm long?

The actual error (0.5cm) is called the *absolute error*
0.5 is 3.6% of 14 – this is the *percentage error*

Use your calculator to find the percentage error when the fraction 22/7 is used to approximate the value of π.
(Hint: Don't forget that your calculator has a π button).

0.04%

Reminder about percentages:
You should be able to do the following types of calculation:

Answers:
2.856
15.3%
2205
15.624
$285.71

What is 12% of 23.8?
What is 56 as a percentage of 365?
Increase 2100 by 5%.
Decrease 18.6 by 16%.
A coat costs $300 including 5% sales tax. What is the cost of the coat before tax?

Estimation: Estimation is an important mathematical skill. Estimating the answer to a problem (especially a practical problem) doesn't mean that you are unable to work out the accurate answer – only that you want to have a *rough* idea of the size of the answer. How long will it take me to fly from Berlin to Rome? It's about 1500km and planes fly at about 800km/h, so the flying time is just under 2 hours – that's an estimate. The actual distance is 1537km, and the plane I am in is actually flying at 825km/h – this gives the flight time as 1.86 hours.

When asked to calculate an estimate, round the numbers to 1 S.F. and you should find the calculation fairly easy to do.

For example, an estimate for $\dfrac{3.8^2 \times 2.1}{7.8}$ is $\dfrac{4^2 \times 2}{8} = 4$ To 3 S.F., the correct answer is 3.89.

You are also expected to be able to assess whether your answers to questions are reasonable, and this requires the application of common sense as well as estimates. Which of the following answers to questions do you think require a rethink?

The height of the building is 2.7m
The area of the triangle is -6cm²
The car was travelling at 68 km/h
The mean weight of an egg is 34kg
He ran 200m in 25 seconds

Standard Form

The exponential expression a^b: You must understand the meaning of negative and fractional powers as well as positive, whole number powers. Let's look at powers of 2:

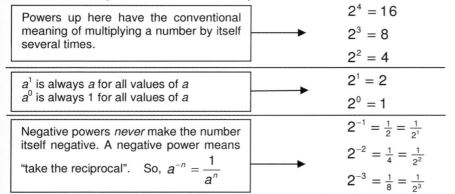

Powers up here have the conventional meaning of multiplying a number by itself several times. →	$2^4 = 16$ $2^3 = 8$ $2^2 = 4$
a^1 is always a for all values of a a^0 is always 1 for all values of a →	$2^1 = 2$ $2^0 = 1$
Negative powers *never* make the number itself negative. A negative power means "take the reciprocal". So, $a^{-n} = \dfrac{1}{a^n}$ →	$2^{-1} = \frac{1}{2} = \frac{1}{2^1}$ $2^{-2} = \frac{1}{4} = \frac{1}{2^2}$ $2^{-3} = \frac{1}{8} = \frac{1}{2^3}$

Fractional powers always involve *roots*. The power $\frac{1}{2}$ means the square root, the power $\frac{1}{3}$ means the cube root; the power $\frac{3}{2}$ means the cube of the square root. These can be combined with a negative sign to give, for example:

$$3^{-\frac{2}{5}} = \frac{1}{(\sqrt[5]{3})^2}$$

In general, $a^{\frac{1}{n}} = \sqrt[n]{a}$ and $a^{\frac{m}{n}} = \left(\sqrt[n]{a}\right)^m = \sqrt[n]{a^m}$

Examples:
$$2.5^1 = 2.5$$
$$4^{-2} = \frac{1}{16}$$
$$\left(\frac{2}{3}\right)^{-3} = \left(\frac{3^3}{2^3}\right) = \frac{27}{8}$$
$$8^{\frac{5}{3}} = \left(\sqrt[3]{8}\right)^5 = 32$$

Standard form: Standard (or scientific) form gives us a way of writing very large and very small numbers without using lots of zeroes. eg:

$$43000 = 4.3 \times 10000 = 4.3 \times 10^4$$
$$23\,000\,000 = 2.3 \times 10\,000\,000 = 2.3 \times 10^7$$
$$0.00056 = 5.6 \times \frac{1}{10000} = 5.6 \times 10^{-4}$$
$$0.000000109 = 1.09 \times \frac{1}{10000000} = 1.09 \times 10^{-7}$$

It is important that the first part of the number is between 1 and 10. If you do a calculation and the answer comes out as 12×10^4 this is not in standard form: it must be written as 1.2×10^5.

- A common mistake is to write eg 4.1×10^3 as 4.1^3

- 🖩 make sure you know how to read and enter numbers in standard form on your calculator.

- To add or subtract, convert numbers back to ordinary form.

To convert to standard form:
- Put the decimal point in position (ie to give a number between 1 and 10).
- Count how many moves to get the decimal point back to its original place.
- Moving to the right → positive power
- Moving to the left → negative power

If $x = 3.6 \times 10^4$ and $y = 1.8 \times 10^{-8}$, calculate the values of x^2 and x/y, giving your answers in the form $a \times 10^n$, where $1 \leq a \leq 10$ and $n \in \mathbb{Z}$.

(The last bit is a fancy way of saying "answers in standard form.")

To multiply, multiply the first parts and add the powers. $(3.6 \times 10^4) \times (3.6 \times 10^4) = \mathbf{1.296 \times 10^9}$

To divide, divide the first parts and subtract the powers. $(3.6 \times 10^4) \div (1.8 \times 10^{-8}) = \mathbf{2 \times 10^{12}}$

Let $s = 81000$ and $t = 0.012$. Write s and t in standard form, and calculate $s \div t$, giving your answer in standard form.

$8.1 \times 10^4,\ 1.2 \times 10^{-2},\ 6.75 \times 10^6$

Units of Measurement

The metric system: The basic units of measurement are:

Quantity	Unit	Symbol
Length	Metre	m
Weight	Gramme	g
Time	Second	s
Liquid volume	Litre	l

Using prefixes, all of these units can be increased or decreased in multiples of 10. The common prefixes are:

Smaller	Power of 10	Bigger
deci (d)	10^1	deca (D)
centi (c)	10^2	hecta (h)
milli (m)	10^3	kilo (k)
micro (μ)	10^6	mega (M)

eg: 1000 millilitres = 1 litre (1000ml = 1l)
100 centimetres = 1 metre (100cm = 1m)
1000 grammes = 1 kilogram (1000g = 1kg)

When the units are combined, use the following notation
eg: Speed = metres per second = ms^{-1}

You will often find standard form useful for converting units. For example, to convert kilometres to millimetres you will need to multiply by 1000 and 1000 again, ie by 10^6. So, 4km = 4×10^6mm.

Areas and volumes: How many cm^2 is $4m^2$? It is tempting to multiply by 100 and say $400cm^2$. However, as we can see from the square, $1m^2 = 100cm^2 \times 100cm^2 = 10000cm^2$.
So, $4m^2 = 4 \times 100 \times 100 = 40000cm^2$. Use a similar calculation for volumes.
eg: $3.1cm^3 = 3.1 \times 10 \times 10 \times 10 = 3100mm^3$

Note that for water, 1ml = $1cm^3$. It follows that 1litre = $1000cm^3$ and, since $1m^3 = 1,000,000cm^3$, $1m^3$ = 1000 litres.

Conversions: How do we convert a speed of, say, $65kmh^{-1}$ to ms^{-1}? 1km = 1000m and 1 hour = 3600s, so the calculation is going to involve multiplications and/or divisions of these numbers. Think like this:

- In 1 hour, the number of metres travelled will be a bigger number than the number of km – so *multiply* by 1000.
- In 1 second, the distance travelled will be less than in 1 hour, so *divide* by 3600.

- $65kmh^{-1} = \dfrac{65 \times 1000}{3600} = 18.1ms^{-1}$

Estimations: Answers can be estimated by using 1 S.F. throughout, and you should try and check that your answers are *reasonable* by doing such an estimate (see page 6).
eg: The radius of the Earth is about 6400km. How fast is a point on the equator travelling in ms^{-1}? The calculation required is:

Required data:
1 day = 24 hours
1 hour = 3600s
1km = 1000m

Required formulae:
$C = 2\pi r$
Speed = distance/time

$$\text{Speed} = \frac{2\pi \times 6400 \times 1000}{24 \times 3600} \approx \frac{6 \times 6000 \times 1000}{20 \times 4000} = \frac{36000}{80} \approx 400ms^{-1}$$

The actual answer is $465.4ms^{-1}$

Currency Conversions

The exchange rate between two currencies is always quoted by comparing 1 unit in one of the currencies with the equivalent amount in the other currency. Use the reciprocal of this rate to work out the rate from the second currency back to the first.

eg: $1 = 2.45 crowns. The reciprocal of 2.45 is $\dfrac{1}{2.45} = 0.408$ so 1 crown = $0.408. Which rate do you use? If, for example, you are asked to convert $62 to crowns, say to yourself: $1 is 2.45 crowns, so $62 is 62 × 2.45 crowns. And the answer is therefore 151.90 crowns.

Commission: Agencies which exchange currency make their money on the deal by making a charge (the commission).The commission rate is often subject to a minimum charge. For example: "Commission is 1.5% or $5, whichever is greater." Using the rates quoted above, how many crowns would we get for $50 and for $500?

- **$50**. 1.5% of $50 is $0.75, so $5 will be charged. We therefore only have $45 to exchange, and this will give us 45 × 2.45 = 110.25 crowns.
- **$500**. 1.5% of $500 is $7.50, so this is the amount charged. We only have $492.50 to exchange, and this will give us 492.5 × 2.45 = 1206.63 crowns.

Spread: Another way of making a profit is to charge different amounts for buying and selling. For example, the quoted rates may be: "We will sell you crowns at $1 = 2.42 crowns and we will buy crowns from you at $1 = 2.48 crowns. To see how this works:

- $1000 can be changed into 1000 × 2.42 = 2420 crowns.
- 2420 crowns can be changed into 2420 ÷ 2.48 = $975.81.

Thus the profit on the deal is $24.19, equivalent to about 2.4%.

Simple and Compound Interest: These topics are discussed on page 10. There are two formulae which can be used, but it is often easier to calculate from basic principles.

| I = amount of interest paid |
| C = the amount of the loan or investment (the "capital") |
| R = the interest rate (as a percentage) |
| N = the number of time periods |

SIMPLE INTEREST FORMULA	COMPOUND INTEREST FORMULA
$I = \dfrac{CRN}{100}$	$I = C\left(1 + \dfrac{R}{100}\right)^N - C$

If you use the compound interest formula, it is important to realise that the amount in the account is $C\left(1 + \dfrac{R}{100}\right)^N$. Subtracting C, the original amount, tells us how much interest has been paid overall. As with all formulae, a question may ask you to calculate the value of a letter other than the one on the left hand side (the amount of interest).

£1000 is invested at an interest rate of 6% per annum compounded yearly.
a)   What is the amount after 3 years?
b)   How many months will £1000 take to increase to £1100 if invested at an interest rate of 6% per annum compounded monthly?

a)   Using the formula, the amount after 3 years is $1000 \times 1.06^3 = £1191.02$
Remember that to increase by 6% you multiply by 1.06. This is reflected in the formula in the term $1 + \dfrac{R}{100}$.

b)   When compounded monthly this is the same as increasing the investment by 0.5% per month. (This is *more* than 6% per year because each 0.5% increase applies to a slightly larger amount as the year progresses). So we need to solve the equation $1000 \times 1.005^N = 1100$; in other words, how many times do we increase by 0.5% before we get £1100?

To solve this, use trial and error on your calculator. You will find that you must carry out 20 increases to double your money, so the answer is **20 months.**

The following is an example of a more general financial question.

When selling a house, an agent receives 2% on the first £30 000 and 1.5% on the remainder of the price of the house as commission.
a)   How much does he receive when selling a house for £330 000?
      2% of 30 000 = $0.02 \times 30\,000 = £600$
There is now £300 000 left, and this will earn commission at 1.5%.
      1.5% of 300 000 = $0.015 \times 300\,000 = £4500$
      Total commission = 600 + 4500 = **£5100**
b)   What is the selling price of the house if the agent receives £1650 as commission?
The first bit of the commission will *always* be 2% of 30 000 = £600.
In this case, this leaves £1050 to go. So the question is: "1050 is 1.5% of what?" Two ways of doing this. Play around on the calculator (ie trial and error) until you get the right answer. Or form an equation (replacing "what" with x).
      1.5% of x = 1050
      $0.015 \times x = 1050$
      $x = 1050/0.015 = 70\,000$
Remember that this is the value of the house *above* £30 000. So the price of the house is 30 000 + 70 000 = **£100 000**
(In this sort of question, it's always worth checking the answer by working forwards as in part (a))

The table shows part of a currency conversion chart. For example GBP 1 is equivalent to $AUS 2.33.

	GBP	$US	$AUS
GBP	1	s	2.33
$US	0.571	1	t
$AUS	0.429	0.751	1

Giving answers correct to 2 decimal places:
a)   Calculate the values of s and t.
      (Remember the reciprocal rule)

b)   Joe has $US 2500 to exchange at a bank.
      i)   If no commission is charged, how much will Joe receive in GBP?
      ii)   Assuming the bank charges 1.3% commission:
            a)   How much in GBP does Joe pay in commission?
            b)   How much in GBP does Joe actually receive for his USD 2500?

      a) $s = 1.75$, $t = 1.33$ b) (i) GBP 1427.50   (ii)(a) GBP 18.56   (ii)(b) GBP 1408.94

▦ If your calculator has a built-in financial package, you should make sure you fully understand how to use the various functions.

Simultaneous Equations

The process of solving equations enables us to find the values of unknown quantities. Commonly, equations are solved using algebra; other methods are sometimes used, including graphical techniques. If there are *two* unknown quantities, we require two equations to find them. Such equations are called *simultaneous* because we are finding the pair of values which will satisfy both equations at the same time, or simultaneously. There are two algebraic methods which are commonly used.

You are expected to solve simultaneous equations using your GDC. The algebraic methods are included here because they are part of your presumed knowledge.

You should try solving both these examples on the calculator using a built-in APP.

Elimination: Elimination is generally used when the pattern of the two equations is the same.

Solve: $2x - 3y = 11$ (1)
       $3x + 5y = 7$ (2)

$6x - 9y = 33$ (3) = (1) × 3   *(Choose multiplications which give*
$6x + 10y = 14$ (4) = (2) × 2   *the same number of x's or y's)*

$19y = -19$ (4) - (3)
$y = -1$

Now we must find x as well. Substitute the value of y into either of the original equations (2) looks easier.

$3x + 5 \times -1 = 7$
$3x = 12$
$x = 4$

So the solution is $x = 4, y = -1$

Note that it is good practice to put the full answer at the end of the question rather than leaving part of it tucked away in the middle.

Substitution: This is a more general method, and is particularly easy to use if at least one of the equations is in the form $y =$ or $x =$.

Solve: $y = 3x - 5$ (1)
       $6x + 2y = -1$ (2)

Substitute (1) into (2)
$7x + 2(3x - 5) = -1$ *Now solve as an ordinary linear equation*
$6x + 6x - 10 = -1$
$12x = 9$
$x = 0.75$

Substitute the value of x into (1)
$y = 3 \times 0.75 - 5$
$y = -2.75$

So the solution is $x = 0.75, y = -2.75$

Graphical solution: Since each of the simultaneous equations (of the type in the examples above) represent straight lines, the point of intersection represents the only value of x and y which fits both equations. ▧ Plot the graphs, and then use the calculator function which finds the point of intersection. The display shows the calculator being used to solve the simultaneous equations $y = 2x - 2$ and $y = 4 - 0.5x$.

The solution is $x = 2.4$ and $y = 2.8$.

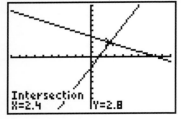

Intersection
X=2.4   Y=2.8

Quadratic Equations

What is a quadratic equation: A quadratic *expression* is in the form $ax^2 + bx + c$, where $a \neq 0$. The following are examples of quadratic expressions:

$$2x^2 - 3x + 5; \quad x^2 - 23; \quad -4x^2; \quad 6x^2 + 2x$$

The simplest quadratic equation is of the form
$$x^2 = 25$$
in which case the solution is
$$x = \pm 5.$$
Don't forget that there are always 2 square roots.

(We deal more with quadratic expressions in the chapter on Mathematical Models, page 58). So equations which involve such expressions are called *quadratic equations*. They are not as simple to solve as linear equations (eg: $2x - 3 = 6$) because it is harder to make x the subject. To further complicate things, there are usually two possible solutions for x. You are only expected to use your GDC to solve quadratic equations (but see page 59 for the factorisation method). As with simultaneous equations, you should be able to use both the built-in APP, and graphical methods.

Quadratic graphs: The graph of $y = ax^2 + bx + c$ will always be a parabola, whatever the values of a, b and c ($a \neq 0$). A parabola is a curve where both sides get ever closer to the vertical.

Terminology: The x values where a graph cuts the axis are known as *zeros* or *roots*.

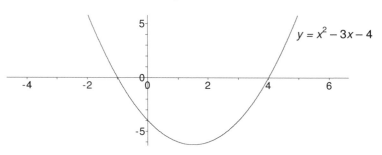

In this case the graph cuts the axis at $x = -1$ and $x = 4$, so these are the solutions of the equation $x^2 - 3x - 4 = 0$. If the graph doesn't cut the x-axis at all, then there are no solutions to the equation (for example, try solving $x^2 + 3x + 3 = 0$); and if it just touches the axis, then there is just one solution (for example, $x^2 - 4x + 4 = 0$).

---

a)   **Draw the graph of $y = x^2 - 2x - 8$.**
b)   **For what range of values of x is $x^2 - 2x - 8$ less than 0?**

b)   Look at the graph:
The y values represent the values of $x^2 - 2x - 8$. When are these values less than 0? When the graph is below the axis. And between what values of x does this happen?

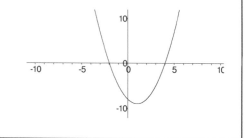

     $-2 < x < 4$

When solving a quadratic equation, you must always ensure that it is first written in the form $ax^2 + bx + c = 0$. The following equation:

$$2x = \frac{6}{x} - 1$$ may not at first look like a quadratic equation, but it can

be rearranged to become $2x^2 + x - 6 = 0$. The solutions of this equation or $x = 1.5$ and $x = -2$. You could try substituting these values into the original equation to check they work. You will need to rearrange to answer the question over the page.

A rectangular garden is fenced on three sides using 80m of fencing. The fourth side is an existing brick wall.

WALL

x

Take x metres to represent the length of one of the sides of the garden at right angles to the wall.

a)   Write an expression, in terms of x, for the length of fence parallel to the wall.
       Hint: Remember that the length of the fence in total is 80m.
b)   Write down an expression, in terms of x for the area of the garden.
c)   Given that the area is 600m^2 form an equation in x, and solve the equation to find the possible values of x.

(a) $80 - 2x$ (b) $x(80 - 2x)$ (c) $x(80 - 2x) = 600$, $x = 10$ or 30

Further equations practice: The following questions should all be answered using your GDC. They are a mixture of simultaneous and quadratic equations.

1.   Solve the following pairs of simultaneous equations:

a) $\begin{cases} x + 2y = 15 \\ 5x - 3y = -3 \end{cases}$

b) $\begin{cases} 2x - y = 9 \\ 2y - x = -6 \end{cases}$

c) $\begin{cases} x + y = 2.5 \\ 3x - 7y = 0.5 \end{cases}$

2.   What are the coordinates of the point where the lines $y = x + 3$ and $y = 3x - 1$ meet?

3.   Solve the following quadratic equations:
a) $x^2 + 4x - 21 = 0$
b) $3x^2 - 5x - 7 = 0$
c) $2x(x - 3) = 4x^2 + 3$
d) $x + 3 = 4 + \dfrac{30}{x}$

Solving by using quadratic factorisation is not specifically in the syllabus, but if you are familiar with the method, then questions such as 3a are easily done.

4.   How many solutions are there for the quadratic equation
       $3x^2 - 6x + k = 0$
when:
a) $k = 4$
b) $k = 3$
c) $k = 2$

ANSWERS:
1.   (a) $x = 3$, $y = 6$ (b) $x = 4$, $y = -1$ (c) $x = 1.8$, $y = 0.7$
2. $(2, 5)$
3.   (a) $x = -7$ or 3 (b) $x = -0.907$ or 2.57
       (c) $x = -0.634$ or -2.37 (d) $x = -5$ or 6
4.   (a) 0 solutions   (b) 1 solution   (c) 2 solutions

Sequences and Series

There are many different types of number sequence. You only need to know about two: the *arithmetic sequence* (AP) and the *geometric sequence* (GP). In an AP each number is the previous number *plus* a constant. In a GP each number is the previous number *multiplied* by a constant.

A *series* is the same as a *sequence* except that the terms are added together: thus a series has a *sum*, whereas a sequence doesn't.

To answer most sequences and series questions, make sure you are familiar with the formulae below. First, the notation:

Examples:

Arithmetic sequences:
3, 5, 7, 9 .....
1.1, 1.3, 1.5, 1.7 .....
11, 7, 3, -1, -5 ......

Geometric Sequences:
1, 3, 9, 27 .....
4, 6, 9, 13.5 .....
12, 6, 3, 1.5, 0.75 .....

a = the first term of the sequence
n = the number of terms in the sequence
l = the last term of the sequence
d = the common difference (the number added on in an AP)
r = the common ratio (the multiplier in a GP)
u_n = the value of the nth term
S_n = the sum of the first n terms

The formulae:
For an AP:

Your formula sheet uses u_1 instead of a.

The value of the nth term: $u_n = a + (n-1)d$

The sum of n terms: $S_n = \dfrac{n}{2}(a+l) = \dfrac{n}{2}(2a + (n-1)d)$

For a GP:

The sum formulae always start from the first term. If you wanted to sum, say, the 10th to the 20th terms, you would calculate $S_{20} - S_9$. Think about it!

The value of the nth term: $u_n = ar^{n-1}$

The sum of n terms: $S_n = \dfrac{a(r^n - 1)}{r-1}$

At the end of 1983 the population of a town was k people. At the end of 1999 the population was $5k$ people after an average increase of 70 people each year. Calculate k.

This is an A.P. because 70 people are *added* each year. Count the number of terms carefully, using your fingers if necessary! – 1999 will be the 17th term.
$u_{17} = k + (17-1) \times 70$ but $u_{17} = 5k$
$5k = k + 1120 \Rightarrow 4k = 1120 \Rightarrow k = 280$

A ball is dropped from a height of 9m. It hits the ground and rebounds to a height of 6m. It falls again, hits the ground and rebounds to a height of 4m. It continues to fall, hit the ground and rebound with its rebound height and fall height in the same ratio.
a)   To what height will it rebound after it next hits the ground?
b)   How many times will it hit the ground before the rebound height becomes less than 9cm?

a) G.P. since the height is multiplied each time. To find the multiplier, divide the second number by the first.
b) Note the change in units. Keep doing the sum on your calculator and count the number of hits on the ground.

2.67m,   12 hits

Simple and Compound Interest

One important application of sequences and series is their use in solving financial problems involving *interest*. If a sum of money is invested, the interest is the amount (expressed as a %) that it earns during each period (usually, but not necessarily, a year).

Simple interest: The interest earned is not added to the amount invested which thus stays constant.

- $1000 at 5% simple interest per year will earn $50/year. In 10 years, the investment is worth 1000 + 10 x 50 = $1500.

Compound interest: The interest earned is *added* to the amount invested. Thus the investment grows by a larger amount each year.

- $1000 at 5% compound interest will multiply by 1.05 each year (A 5% increase can be calculated using a multiplier of 1.05).

After 1 year, the investment is worth 1000 x 1.05 = $1050
After 2 years, the investment is worth 1050 x 1.05 = $1102.50
After *n* years, the investment is worth 1000×1.05^n

Note that with the simple interest, the value of the investment is increased by $50/year and will form an AP. With the compound interest, the value will x 1.05 each year and will form a GP.

> Beware of questions where extra money is added to the investment each year *as well as* the interest.

John deposits $2500 with a bank which pays compound interest at a rate of 5% each year. Calculate the interest he receives at the end of four years.

His investment will be worth 2500×1.05^4 = $3038.77. So the amount of interest he has received will be 3038.77 − 2500 = **$538.77**

Amy invests $2500 with a company that pays simple interest annually. Calculate the rate of interest the company must pay in order that Amy receives the same interest as John after 4 years.

The amount of simple interest is the same each year, so it must be 538.77 ÷ 4 = $134.69. We now need this as a percentage of the investment.

$$\frac{134.69}{2500} \times 100 = \textbf{5.39\%}$$

Tino deposits $2000 into an investment account that pays 5% interest per annum.
a) What will be the value of the investment after 6 years if the interest is reinvested
(ie 5 years at 5% compound interest)

b) How many years would it take the investment to double in value.
(Keep multiplying by 1.05 on your calculator)

c) At the beginning of the each year Brenda deposits $2000 into an investment account that pays 5% interest per annum. Interest is calculated annually and reinvested. How much would be in the account after 6 years.
(Don't worry about formulae: multiply by 1.05, then add 2000. Do this until 5 years are up).

$2680.19, 15 years, $14284.02

A loan of $4000 at a rate of 12% per annum is compounded monthly. How much will it cost if the loan is to be repaid in 1 year?

Each month 1% interest is added to the loan, so the total for the year will be more than 12%.
Cost for 1 year = 4000×1.01^{12} = **4507.30**

What is the equivalent simple interest rate?

Total interest = $507.30, so the rate is $\frac{507.30}{4000} \times 100 = \textbf{12.7\%}$

Depreciation: Depreciation is the amount an asset loses in value each year, and works a bit like compound interest in reverse. For example, the value of a new car might depreciate by 30% each year: the amount of depreciation will reduce each year since it will be 30% of a smaller amount each time. If the car was bought for $15000, the depreciation will be 30% of $15000 = $4500 during the first year, leaving the car worth $10500 at the end of the year. During year 2, the depreciation will be 30% of $10500 = $3150; the car will then be worth $7350. Note that the calculation could be done in one step as 15000×0.70^2 (since a 30% decrease equates to a multiplier of 0.70).

For tax purposes, a landlord who rents out a flat can depreciate its furniture by 10% per annum. When new, he paid £3600 for the furniture. What is it worth, to the nearest pound, after 5 years?

$3600 \times 0.90^5 = £2125.76$. To the nearest pound, **£2126.**

Further sequences and series practice:
1. a)   Using a for the first term of an arithmetic sequence, and d for the common difference, write down formulae in a and d for the sum of the first four terms, and the sum of the first ten terms.
    b)   If the sum of the first four terms is 336, and the sum of the **next** six terms is 384, find the values of a and d.

2. $2500 is invested at 4% compounded annually.
    a)   How much will it be worth after 5 years?
    b)   How long will it take for the investment to double?

3. a)   A geometric sequence has first term 3 and common ratio 4. What is the value of the 9th term?
    b)   Another geometric sequence has first term 4 and common ratio 3. Which term in the sequence will be the first whose value exceeds that found in part (a)?
    Hint: One way of doing this is to set up a function on your GDC for the nth term, and then create a table of values starting with n = 1.

4. I bought an artwork 12 years ago for $10000. It appreciated in value by 4% per year for 6 years, and then depreciated by 4% per year for the next 6 years. What is it now worth?

5. (a)   Find the total interest earned over 5 years when €1800 is invested at an annual interest rate of 4.2% compounded monthly.
    Hint: Divide the interest rate by 12 to find the monthly rate. Why is this different from using an annual rate of 4.2%?
    (b)   How much less interest would be earned if the annual rate was not compounded monthly?

ANSWERS

1.   (a) $4a + 6d$, $10a + 45d$ (b) $a = 144$, $d = -40$
2.   (a) $3041.63   (b) 18 years
3.   (a) 196608   (b)11th term
4. $9904.38 *(Each 4% decrease is 4% of a slightly larger amount than each of the 4% increases).*
5.   (a) €419.81   (b) €8.70

DESCRIPTIVE STATISTICS

Basics of Statistics

Definitions: A *population* is a set from which *statistics* are drawn. A *sample* is a subset drawn from the population. Sample statistics (such as the mean) can be used to estimate population statistics. *Discrete* data are restricted to certain values only (often integers) whereas *continuous* data can take any values. The *frequency* is the number of times a particular value occurs. A *frequency table* shows how often each value occurs in a discrete distribution. In a continuous distribution, it is necessary to use a *grouped* frequency table. Numerical data is usually collected into a table and then split into *groups* or *classes*. The *boundaries* of the classes must be dealt with carefully, especially for continuous data. Consider a table of weights (see right): into which class would a weight of 10kg be put? It would be better if the first group were labelled as $0 \le w < 10$ and the second as $10 \le w < 20$ and then 10 would fall into the second group. The *interval width* in this case is 10, and the *mid-interval value* of the first group is 5 and so on.

Examples of populations:
People who live in Europe
People who drive
Apples grown in France
Cars made in 2001

Examples of discrete data:
Shoe sizes
Goals scored by a team
Number of chocolates in a box

Examples of continuous data
Weights of people
Athletes' times to run 100m
Heights of mountains

Weight (kg)
0 - 10
10 - 20

Frequency Diagrams: Data can be appreciated more when displayed in a diagram. *Frequency histograms* (bar charts) are a simple way to display both discrete and continuous data, and are very easy to construct. A frequency histogram uses equal class intervals. If the data is continuous, there cannot be gaps between the bars.

This table lists the heights of 55 children:

131	136	142	145	153	144	140	145	137	136	140
133	133	146	144	138	134	142	142	149	147	136
152	148	142	143	144	134	134	147	141	139	144
135	135	150	137	132	139	141	149	131	148	136
132	137	138	143	142	140	150	149	145	147	144

The frequency table and frequency histogram are shown below:

Height h (cm)	Frequency
$130 < h \le 135$	10
$135 < h \le 140$	15
$140 < h \le 145$	17
$145 < h \le 150$	11
$150 < h \le 155$	2
Total	55

Measures of Central Tendency: One of the most basic statistics which can be used as a figure to represent the whole group is an average. You are required to know three different averages: the *mean*, *mode* and the *median*.

Mean: To calculate the mean, add all the numbers together and divide by the number of values. If the data is in a frequency table then the total value is calculated by multiplying each value by its frequency and totalling the result. Note that the number of values is *not* the number of classes, but the sum of the frequencies.

Pupils absent (x)	No of days (f)	fx
0	20	0
1	4	4
2	3	6
3	3	9
TOTAL	30	19

The table shows the number of days of absence during a term for the pupils in a particular class. For example, 2 pupils have a total absence of 3 days each.

We can see that there are a total of 19 days absence over a period of 30 days. So the mean number of days absent was 19/30 = 0.63 (It is a common mistake to divide 19 by 4, the number of classes).

⊞ You should know how to enter a frequency table into your GDC, and use the data to find the mean.

If the data is presented in a grouped frequency table, the same procedure is followed except that the mid-interval value of each group is used to represent the x value for each group. This means that the *actual* data values are unknown and in this case the mean is only an estimate. "Calculate an estimate of the mean" does *not* mean that you make a guess!

Always check if the answer is "reasonable." Look at the distribution of weights – does 30.7 look like the mean?

Weight of apples (w)	No of apples (f)	Mid interval (x)	fx
$20 \le w < 25$	12	22.5	270
$25 \le w < 30$	20	27.5	550
$30 \le w < 35$	25	32.5	812.5
$35 \le w < 40$	17	37.5	637.5
TOTAL	74		2270

Estimated mean weight of an apple is
$$\frac{2270}{74} = 30.7g$$

Mode: The mode is the value that occurs most often. In a frequency table, it is the value with the highest frequency. In a grouped frequency table, the best you can do is say which *class* has the highest frequency – this is called the *modal class* or *modal group*. The modal class above is $30 \le w < 35$ g.

Median: If a set of values is listed in ascending order, the middle value is the *median*. It is another type of average: there are as many values above the median as below it. Unlike the mean, it is unaffected by extra large or extra small values. In the following list there are 15 values so the 8th is the middle one (7 below it, 7 above it.

1 1 3 5 6 6 6 **7** 7 9 10 10 12 15 18   Median = 7

If there are an even number of values, find the mean of the middle two to calculate the median.

24 26 27 **27 29** 30 30 33   Median = 28

⊞ Note that your GDC will not give accurate values for the median from a grouped frequency table. In such cases you will need to use a cumulative frequency graph as described in the next section.

For the set of marks {7, 4, 2, 11, 2, 5, 10, 12, 2, 5}
a)   Calculate the mean;
b)   Find the mode;
c)   Find the median. *(Remember to put them in order first).*

6,   2,   5

The annual salaries of employees in a small company are given in the table.

Category (x)	Number of employees (f)	Salary	fx
Trainees	8	£10000	80000
Computer Operators	6	£15300	91800
Secretaries	8	£16200	129600
Salesmen	9	£24000	216000
Managers	3	£31500	94500
TOTAL	34		611900

a)   What is the modal salary?
b)   Calculate the mean salary to 3 significant figures.

(The original table had the first three columns. I have added the fourth and the totals row).
a)   Modal salary is **£24000** since more people earn it than any other.
b)   Mean salary = 611900 ÷34 = £17997.06 = **£18000 to 3SF**

---

25 children were asked to identify 5 famous people from a set of photographs. The table shows the number of correct answers they gave.

Number of correct answers	0	1	2	3	4	5
Frequency	4	3	8	a	4	1

a) Find the value of a.
b) Use your GDC to find:
   (i)   The mean number of correct answers.
   (ii) The median number of correct answers.

(a) **5**   (b) (i) **2.2**   (ii) **2**

Cumulative Frequency

Cumulative frequency tables: It is easier to calculate the median from a frequency table if it is first converted into a *cumulative frequency table.* Whether the data is discrete or continuous, the method is the same. Each value of cumulative frequency measures how many x values there are in total up to that point. Consider the following grouped frequency table:

This table uses the convention that 0 - means: "from 0 up to the next value" (5 in this case).

x	0 -	5 -	10 -	15 -	20 -	25 - 30
f	4	11	17	25	14	4

If we now find the number of x values *up to* the top value in each group, we get the following cumulative frequency table:

Note that in the conversion to the grouped frequency table, the "up to" points are the **top** of each group

x	<5	<10	<15	<20	<25	<30
$c.\ f.$	4	15	32	57	71	75

Now we plot the points (5, 4), (10, 15) and so on.

The points in the table are plotted and are joined either by straight lines or a smooth curve. To find the median, a line is drawn to the right from 38 (the middle value of the distribution) and down to the x axis. The median can be seen to be about 16.

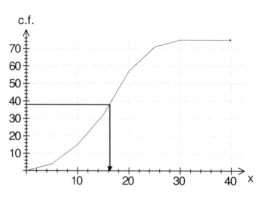

Quartiles: 50% of the population lie above the median, 50% below. We can also divide the population into *quartiles*: 25% lie below the first quartile, 50% below the second (which is also the median) 75% below the third quartile. There are 75 results in the previous table, so the first quartile will be the 19th result (19 is about one quarter of 75). Looking at the graph, this gives the first quartile as 11 and the third quartile (the 57th result) as 20. Similarly, the distribution can be divided into 100 parts knows as *percentiles*. "Your test result is in the top 5 percentiles of the population" means that at least 95% of people scored worse than you did.

At a school athletics meeting the times for running 200m were entered in a table.

Time (to nearest second)	26	27	28	29	30
Number of boys	7	17	16	14	6

a) **Complete the cumulative frequency table for these results.**

Time in seconds	Number of boys
<26.5	7
<27.5	
<28.5	
<29.5	
<30.5	

b) **The fastest 20% of boys qualify to enter a regional competition. Estimate the slowest qualifying time.** *(There are 60 boys. Estimate the time of the 48th boy from a cumulative frequency graph).*

24, 40, 54, 60   29.1s

A biologist recorded as a frequency distribution the diameters (*D*), measured to the nearest millimetre, of 100 rose petals. The result are given in the table below.

Diameter of petal	Number of petals	Diameter of petal	Cum. frequency
$27 < L \leq 29$	2	≤ 29	2
$29 < L \leq 31$	4	≤ 31	6
$31 < L \leq 33$	8	≤ 33	14
$33 < L \leq 35$	21	≤ 35	35
$35 < L \leq 37$	30	≤ 37	65
$37 < L \leq 39$	18	≤ 39	83
$39 < L \leq 41$	12	≤ 41	95
$41 < L \leq 43$	5	≤ 43	100
	100		

a) **Construct a cumulative frequency table for the data.** (Completed in grey).
b) **Draw a cumulative frequency curve and use it to estimate the median, the lower and upper quartiles.**

a) Draw a line from 50 on the *y*-axis to the graph then down to the *x*-axis. This will be the median.
Median = 36cm

b) For the quartiles, do the same as for the median, except that you take the lines from the 25 and the 75.
Lower quartile = 34cm   Upper quartile = 38
(These results are to the nearest centimetre)

Note that the construction lines do not *have* to be shown, but the examiner will like to see them.

Box and Whisker Plots: Why are there so many different ways of presenting data? Because although tables and diagrams are much easier to interpret than raw data, different types of presentation allow for a variety of analyses of the data to be made. A box and whisker plot shows the following information:

- Extreme values
- Lower quartile
- Median
- Upper quartile.

The box plot for the data on bushes treated with fertiliser (see right) looks like this.

Fruit yield from 20 bushes (in kg):	
Treated bushes	Untreated bushes
22 37 41 55 52	20 37 27 50 12
19 32 39 44 40	26 21 46 31 49
50 28 44 38 24	13 21 40 18 28
40 31 43 47 54	26 39 24 33 48

What information can we read from this box plot? Apart from the actual values of the quartiles and the medain, we see that the extreme values are not too far from the bulk of the values as represented by the box (the middle 50% of values). The median is slightly to the right of centre implying that there are more values towards the upper end of the distribution.

Box plots are particularly useful when set against each other. For example, we can compare the yields for both treated and untreated bushes:

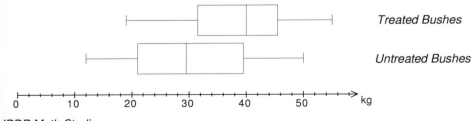

Treated Bushes

Untreated Bushes

Measures of Dispersion

The most useful summary statistics for a set of data are the "average" (mean or median; mode is not representative of all the data), and the *spread*. Such a measure gives an indication of how the data is dispersed around the average.

Range: The range is the difference between the highest and lowest values. It is a crude measure of spread since it does not take the other values into account at all.

Interquartile range: The IQR is the difference between the first and third quartiles (the 25th and 75th percentiles). This gives us the spread of the middle 50% of values, and thus leaves out possible extreme values at each end. On a box plot, the IQR is the length of the box (as measured against the scale). The box plots on the previous page give an IQR of 14 for the treated bushes, 18.5 for the untreated bushes, indicating that treated bushes give a more *consistent* yield. (Remember that word for exam questions).

Standard deviation: The standard deviation is, roughly, the average deviation of all the values from the mean. Unlike the IQR, which only depends on the middle 50% of values, the standard deviation uses all the values. ▤ You must know how to put data values into your calculator (including in the form a frequency table) and then read off the mean and standard deviation.

You can also read off the median and the quartiles from your calculator display – but not if you have input the mid-interval values of a grouped distribution.

Try calculating the standard deviation of the weight of peanuts in these 80 packets:

Weight	No of packets
$80 \leq W < 85$	5
$85 \leq W < 90$	10
$90 \leq W < 95$	15
$95 \leq W < 100$	26
$100 \leq W < 105$	13
$105 \leq W < 110$	7
$110 \leq W < 115$	4

You will need to use the mid-interval values to represent each group.

A class takes a mathematics test. The mean score is 65%, and the standard deviation is 8%. This means that most of the scores will be in the range 49% - 81%.

You should find that the mean weight is 96.8 and the standard deviation is 7.41.

As a rough indicator, the majority of results in a reasonably symmetrical distribution are within two standard deviations of the mean.

▤ Different calculators use different statistical notation, and these may differ from that used in the IB. Make sure you understand which to use on your own GDC.

The mean number of children per female for a group of 25 women was 1.3 and the standard deviation was 1.08. For a second group of 25 the mean was 2.2 and the standard deviation 2.1. Describe the differences between the numbers of children for the two groups.

The second group has almost twice as many children per female as the first group. In addition, the dispersion is greater, indicating that some people in the second group have quite large numbers of children.

(Note: using the "two standard deviation test", the range for the first group is −0.86 to 3.46 (in practice, 0 to 3) and for the second group is −2 to 6.4 (in practice 0 to 6).

Further statistics practice:

1. The histogram on the right shows the number of hours a professional musician practises each day during April:

    a) Write down the modal number of hours.

    b) Calculate the mean number of hours he practises each day.

    c) Find the standard deviation.

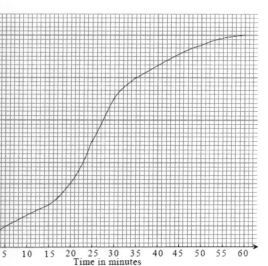

2. The cumulative frequency graph (left) has been drawn from a frequency table showing the time it takes a number of students to complete a computer game.

    a) Find the median.
    b) Find the interquartile range.

The graph has been drawn using the data in the following frequency table:

Time (min)	$0<x\le5$	$5<x\le15$	$15<x\le20$	$20<x\le25$	$25<x\le35$	$35<x\le50$	$50<x\le60$
No. of students	20	20	a	40	60	b	10

    c) Using the graph, find the values of a and b.
    d) Calculate an estimate of the mean time taken to complete the computer game.

3. The following table shows the number of errors per page in a 100 page document.

Number of errors	0	1	2	3	4	5
Number of pages	28	22	18	14	12	6

a) State whether the data is discrete or continuous.
b) Draw a histogram to represent the data.
c) Find the mean number of errors per page.
d) Find the median number of errors per page.
e) Write down the modal number of errors per page.

ANSWERS

1. a) 6
    b) 6.1
    c) 1.22

2. a) 25
    b) 14
    c) $a = 20, b = 30$
    d) 25.6

3. a) Discrete
    c) 1.78
    d) 1.5
    e) 0

3. (b)

LOGIC, SETS AND PROBABILITY
Basics of Symbolic Logic

Propositions: The building block of logic is the *proposition*. This is a statement that can have one of two values, *true* or *false*. "I paint pictures" and "$x > 4$" are propositions, whereas "What is the time?" and "$2x - 3$" are not. Propositions can be denoted by a small letter.

Logic does not really concern itself with whether the propositions are *actually* true or false – only the reasoning leading from one proposition to the next.

eg: p: $x > 4$ reads as "p is the proposition that $x > 4$"

Negation: The *negation* of a proposition is formed by putting in words such as "not" or "do not." Its symbol is ¬.

- p: "I paint pictures"   ¬p: "I do not paint pictures"
- p: "The train is late"   ¬p: "The train is not late"
- p: $x > 4$ ¬p: $x \leq 4$

Note that negation is not the same as "opposite." For example:

- p: "The glass is full"   ¬p: "The glass is not full"

You could not use "The glass is empty" because if the glass is not full, it could still have *some* water in it.

Truth tables: A truth table shows how the values (ie true or false) of a set of propositions affect the values of other propositions. The truth table for negation looks like this:

P	¬p
T	F
F	T

The first column shows all the possible values of p (ie true or false). The second column shows the corresponding values of ¬p. So take, for example, p: "The sun is shining". If p is true, and the sun is shining, then the proposition ¬p (ie "the sun is not shining") must be false, and vice versa.

Conjunction: The word *and* can be used to join two propositions together. Its symbol is ∧. For example:

- p: x is a positive even number. q: $x < 10$
- $p \wedge q$: x is a positive number and $x < 10$.

Note that we now need 4 rows to show all the possible combinations of values of p and q

Clearly this combined proposition is only true when *both* of the original propositions are true. In other words, its truth table is:

P	q	p∧q
T	T	T
T	F	F
F	T	F
F	F	F

Disjunction (alternation):
The word *or* can also be used to join propositions. "Or" can mean two things: "One or the other or both" (disjunction with symbol ∨) or "one or the other but *not* both" (exclusive disjunction with symbol <u>∨</u>) Look carefully at their truth tables.

P	q	p ∨ q	p <u>∨</u> q
T	T	T	F
T	F	T	T
F	T	T	T
F	F	F	F

Which of these two statements is disjunction, and which is exclusive disjunction?

- Your birthday party will either be this Saturday or next Saturday.
- This course requires you to have either a 5 in English or a 6 in History.

Only FF will give F when drawing up a truth table for ∨

P	q	¬p	¬p∨q
T	T	F	T
T	F	F	F
F	T	T	T
F	F	T	T

What is the truth table for the statement ¬$p \vee q$? We start by drawing up the first two columns as in the truth tables above, then drawing a third column for ¬p. Now we look at columns ¬p and q: when they are both false, ¬$p \vee q$ is false, otherwise it is true.

Implication

If...then...:   Under what conditions is the proposition *r:* "If you steal then you will go to prison" true? Clearly if you *do* steal and you *do* go to prison, then *r* is true. However, if you steal and you *don't* go to prison (perhaps the judge was feeling lenient) then *r* is false. If you *don't* steal that does not change the truth of *r*. Proposition *r* is an example of *implication*. The two propositions:

* *p*: "You steal"
* *q*: "You go to prison"

are joined by the words "if....then..." and the symbol is $\Rightarrow$. In other words, $r = p \Rightarrow q$ with truth table as shown on the right. The way to remember this truth table is that the row with TF $\rightarrow$ F, otherwise we get T.

P	*q*	$p \Rightarrow q$
T	T	T
T	F	F
F	T	T
F	F	T

Other possible wordings for $p \Rightarrow q$ are:
* *p* only if *q*
* *p* is sufficient for *q*
* *q* is necessary for *p*

eg: *p*: "*x* is a multiple of 4"   *q*: "*x* is even"
$p \Rightarrow q$: "If *x* is a multiple of 4 then *x* is even" or
        "*x* is a multiple of 4 only if *x* is even" or
        "*x* is a multiple of 4 is sufficient for *x* to be even" or
        "*x* is even is necessary for *x* to be a multiple of 4"

Converse, inverse and contrapositive: Consider the following propositions:

* *p*: *x* = 16
* *q*: *x* is a square number

If *x* = 16 then *x* is a square number, so $p \Rightarrow q$ is true. But if *x* is square, does it follow that it is 16? This is the *converse* $q \Rightarrow p$ and is clearly not true. The *inverse* is $\neg p \Rightarrow \neg q$, ie If $x \neq 16$ then *x* is not a square number. Again, this is not true. But the *contrapositive*, which is $\neg q \Rightarrow \neg p$ (If *x* is not a square number then $x \neq 16$) *is* true. Let's put all these in one big truth table, remembering that the $\Rightarrow$ sign only gives false in a true/false row (the arrow shows one example of this):

p	*q*	$\neg p$	$\neg q$	$p \Rightarrow q$	$q \Rightarrow p$	$\neg p \Rightarrow \neg q$	$\neg q \Rightarrow \neg p$
T	T	F	F	T	T	T	T
T	F	F	T	F	T	T	F
F	T	T	F	T	F	F	T
F	F	T	T	T	T	T	T

Implication and contrapositive have the same truth tables, so they are equivalent statements (that's why the contrapositive is true when the implication is true). It can also be seen that the converse and the inverse are equivalent. eg:

p: "I am wet"
q: "It is raining"
$p \Rightarrow q$ is not true (I could be wet because I have had a swim). However, if the statement $q \Rightarrow p$ ("If it is raining then I am wet") is true, then so is the inverse $\neg p \Rightarrow \neg q$ ("If I am not wet then it is not raining").

a) Complete the truth table given below:

p	q	$\neg p$	$p \Rightarrow q$	$q \Rightarrow \neg p$
T	T	F	T	F
T	F	F	F	T
F	T	T	T	T
F	F	T	T	T

b) If p is true, what can you say about $(p \Rightarrow q) \wedge (q \Rightarrow \neg p)$?

This looks hard, but it breaks down quite easily. The two propositions in brackets are the ones for which we have just completed the truth tables. Now, what is the truth table for $\wedge$? Always false except in the row with TT, ie TT $\rightarrow$ T. This happens in both of the last two rows. But we are told that p is true, and this happens only in the *first* two rows – these rows finish with TF and FT, so the $\wedge$ is always false. So: $(p \Rightarrow q) \wedge (q \Rightarrow \neg p)$ **is false if p is true**.

(Note that we are dealing with pure logic – we do not need to know what p and q actually are).

---

a) Complete the truth table for:
r: $x > 4$
s: $x^2 > 16$

r	s	$\neg r$	$\neg r \vee s$
T	T		
T	F		
F	T		
F	F		

b) Using the results of part (a), is $\neg r \vee s$ true, or false, when:

i) $x > 4$ and $x^2 \ngtr 16$

ii) $x \ngtr 4$ and $x^2 > 16$ |The symbol $\ngtr$ means "not greater than."

i) **False**   ii) **True**

---

p: x is a multiple of 6; q: x is a multiple of 5; r: x is a factor of 60

a) i) Write a sentence, in words, for the statement: $(q \vee r) \wedge \neg p$

The problem is the bracket: generally, in statements, "and" takes precedence over "or", but we need to bracket the q and the r. Here's one possibility, with the "or" understood to be inclusive:

"x is a multiple of 5 or a factor of 60, and x is not a multiple of 6."

ii) Write in logic notation: "If x is a factor of 60 then it is either not a multiple of 6 or it is a multiple of 5."

We can see an if...then.. in the sentence, so we go for implication: $r \Rightarrow \neg p \vee q$

b) i) Complete the truth table to determine the truth values of each of the following two statements: $(q \vee r) \wedge \neg p$; $r \Rightarrow p \vee \neg q$

The columns are methodically built up to produce the complex statements. Remember the basics: For $\wedge$, TT $\rightarrow$ T, otherwise F; for $\vee$, FF $\rightarrow$ F, otherwise T; for $\Rightarrow$, TF $\rightarrow$ F otherwise T.

p	q	r	$\neg p$	$q \vee r$	$(q \vee r) \wedge \neg p$	$\neg q$	$p \vee \neg q$	$r \Rightarrow p \vee \neg q$
T	T	T	F	T	F	F	T	T
T	T	F	F	T	F	F	T	T
T	F	T	F	T	F	T	T	T
T	F	F	F	F	F	T	T	T
F	T	T	T	T	T	F	F	F
F	T	F	T	T	T	F	F	F
F	F	T	T	T	T	T	T	T
F	F	F	T	F	F	T	T	T

ii) a) List the combinations of truth values of p, q and r that make the statement $(q \vee r) \wedge \neg p$ true. **FTT, FTF and FFT**

b) Write down a possible value of x for each of these combinations of truth values.

We now need to compare the truth values with the original statements. Possible values of x are: For FTT, $x = 10$. For FTF, $x = 25$. For FFT, $x = 3$

Equivalence, Tautology and Contradiction

Equivalence: If two statements have the same truth tables then they are true and false under exactly the same conditions. In this case they are *equivalent* statements. The symbol is $\Leftrightarrow$ and the wording is one of:

- if and only if
- is necessary and sufficient

The symbol shows that p and q are equivalent if both their implication and converse are true.

eg: p: "x is a multiple of 2" ; q: "x is even"

P	q	p⇔q
T	T	T
T	F	F
F	T	F
F	F	T

Clearly both $p \Rightarrow q$ and $q \Rightarrow p$ are both true, so $p \Leftrightarrow q$ and we can write "x is a multiple of 2 if and only if x is even." The *if* works forwards, and the *only if* works backwards.

A question might ask under what conditions two complex statements are equivalent. We build up their truth tables, and where they have *different* truth values, we say that those rows are not allowed. (eg: The answer might be "equivalent except when p is true, q is false and r is true").

---

p: The car is old   q: The car is not green   r: The car is a station wagon.

a)   Express in logic notation
    i)   The car is not old.
    (ii)   The car is green if and only if it is not old and a station wagon
b)   Write the following statement as a sentence in words $(\neg r \wedge q) \Rightarrow \neg p$

a) $\neg p$, $\neg q \Leftrightarrow \neg p \wedge r$ (b) If the car is not a station wagon and is green then it is not old.
(Be safe: don't try and make the English better. eg: "Not a station wagon and not green" is not the same as saying "not a green station wagon.")

Tautology and contradiction: A tautology is a statement that *always* has the value true, whatever the values of the original propositions. ie its truth table is all T's. And a contradiction is *always* false, its truth table being all F's. For example, the truth table for : $(p \Rightarrow q) \Leftrightarrow (p \wedge \neg q)$ is:

p	q	p⇒q	¬q	p∧¬q	(p⇒q)⇔(p∧¬q)
T	T	T	F	F	F
T	F	F	T	T	F
F	T	T	F	F	F
F	F	T	T	F	F

So the statement is a contradiction – it is never true.

Further practice with truth tables:

1.   Given the following propositions:
        p: He works hard
        q: He is happy
        r: He is wealthy
    write each of the following statements in words.
    a) $p \vee q$
    b) $p \Rightarrow (q \wedge r)$
    c) $\neg(q \wedge r)$
    State in words the inverse of $r \Rightarrow q$.

2. Consider the following propositions:

> *p*: I am ill
> *q*: I have a good appetite

a) Write in words $p \vee q$

b) Write in both symbols and words the converse of $p \Rightarrow \neg q$

c) Complete the truth table below for $p \Rightarrow \neg q$

p	*q*	$\neg q$	$p \Rightarrow \neg q$
T	T		
T	F		
F	T		
F	F		

3. Complete the truth table below:

p	*q*	$\neg p$	$p \Rightarrow q$	$q \Rightarrow \neg p$
T	T	F		
T	F	F		
F	T	T		
F	F	T		

If *p* is true, what can you say about $(p \Rightarrow q) \wedge (q \Rightarrow \neg p)$?

4. Complete the following truth table:

p	*q*	$\neg p$	$p \Rightarrow q$	$\neg p \vee q$
T	T	F		
T	F	F		
F	T	T		
F	F	T		

What can you say about $(p \Rightarrow q) \Leftrightarrow (\neg p \vee q)$?

5. By drawing up a truth table, determine whether the compound proposition $\neg p \Rightarrow (p \Rightarrow q)$ is a contradiction, a tautology or neither.

ANSWERS

1. a) He works hard, or he is happy, or both.
   b) If he works hard then he is happy and wealthy.
   c) It is not true that he is happy and wealthy.
   d) If he is not wealthy then he is not happy.

2. a) Either I am ill or I have a good appetite.
   b) $\neg q \Rightarrow p$
      If I do not have a good appetite then I am ill.
   c) F, T, T, T

3. T, F, T, T; F, T, T, T; Contradiction.

4. T, F, T, T; T, F, T, T; Tautology.

5.

p	*q*	$\neg p$	$p \Rightarrow q$	$\neg p \Rightarrow (p \Rightarrow q)$
T	T	F	T	T
T	F	F	F	T
F	T	T	T	T
F	F	T	T	T

Tautology.

Basics of Set Theory

Definitions and notation: Set theory encompasses a wide range of mathematical (and non-mathematical) fields, and it has its own language. A set is any collection of things with a common property: it can be *finite* (eg: set of students in a class) or infinite (eg: set of integers). A set is denoted by a capital letter, and can be defined in words or as a list.

- A = even numbers between 1 and 9
- A = {2, 4, 6, 8}

or a special notation can be used:

- A = {x | x is an even number between 1 and 9}. This would be read as: "The set A is a list of things called x where x is an even number between 1 and 9."

Note the use of "curly brackets" to list the members of a set.

You must be familiar with the following list of symbols:

Symbol	Meaning	Example
U	universal set	U = all the books on my bookshelf.
$\in$	is a member of	E = even numbers; $4 \in A$
$\notin$	is not a member of	E = even numbers; $5 \notin A$
'	complementary set	E = even numbers, E' = odd numbers
$\varnothing$	empty (null) set	A = odd numbers divisible by 2; $A = \varnothing$
$\cap$	intersection	B = multiples of 2; C = multiples of 3 $B \cap C$ = multiples of 6
$\cup$	union	T = tea drinkers; C = coffee drinkers $T \cup C$ = those who drink tea or coffee or both
$\subset$	is a subset of	F = multiples of 4; T = multiples of 2; $F \subset T$
$n(A)$	number of elements in set A	A = {1,3,6,8,9}; $n(A) = 5$

Brackets can be used with the same meaning as in algebra. Thus, $(A \cap B)'$ = the complement of set $A \cap B$, but:
$A' \cap B'$ = the complement of set A $\cap$ the complement of set B
The difference between these can be seen if we define

$$U = \{1,2,3,4,5,6\}, \quad A = \{2,5,6\}, \quad B = \{1,2,3,4\}$$

So, A' = {1,3,4}, B' = {5,6} and $A \cap B$ = {2}
Thus, $(A \cap B)'$ = {1,3,4,5,6} but $A' \cap B' = \varnothing$

Sentences: Set notation can be translated into English sentences, but to have meaning they need a "verb". The equivalents to verbs are: =, ≠, $\in$, $\notin$, $\subset$, $\not\subset$

U = {members of 1997 IB class in school X}
F = {members who play football}
M = {members who passed the last math test}
L = {members who speak three languages}

a) Express as sentences: (i) $L \cup F = U$ (ii) $L \cap M = M$
i) $L \cup F$ are all those who either speak 3 languages or play football or both. Since this group is equal to the whole class, it follows that: **"Everyone in the class either speaks 3 languages or plays football or both."** (It's a bit cumbersome as a sentence, but could be a lot worse)!
ii) $L \cap M$ are those who both passed the test and speak 3 languages. Since this is exactly the same group who passed the test, we know that: **"All those who passed the test speak 3 languages."** (It is also true that $M \subset L$, and this equivalent to $L \cap M = M$).

b) Express in set language: "There is no-one who speaks 3 languages and plays football."
Putting this partially into set language we can say: "The set of those who speak 3 languages and play football is empty." So, $L \cap F = \varnothing$. Note that $L \neq F$ is not the same at all – it simply says that the set of those speaking 3 languages is different from the set of those who play football.

Venn Diagrams

Venn diagrams are excellent for forming a picture of the relationships between sets.

In a room there are 20 people. 11 have black hair, 6 have glasses. 2 people have both black hair and glasses. Imagine that we draw two circles on the floor labelled "black hair" and "glasses" and ask the people to stand in the appropriate circle. The circles will have to overlap to allow for the two people with both. The numbers of people in each region of the room will be:

This is a Venn Diagram. The "room" represents the universal set – for a particular question, there is nothing outside. Each circle represents a set, the overlap is the intersection.

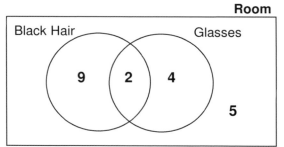

Points to note when filling in the numbers in a Venn Diagram:

A ∩ B'

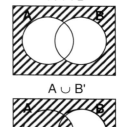

- Start at the centre. If you are not told how many in the intersection, work it out like this: suppose you know there are 15 people in total in the two circles, 10 in circle A and 8 in circle B. 10 + 8 = 18, 3 more than 15 – there are 3 in the intersection.

A' ∩ B'

- When we were told that there were 11 people with black hair, this *includes* those with both black hair and glasses. Same with the 6 people with glasses.

Don't forget to fill in the outer region – although in some questions this set will be "empty."

A ∪ B'

The diagrams on the left show how a Venn diagram can be shaded to show various sets. To find an intersection, you can shade the two sets in different directions, and the intersection will be the area with cross shading. To find a union, shade the two sets in the same direction – the union is the complete shaded area.

Special cases:

Alternatives to B ⊂ A are:
A ∩ B = B
A ∪ B = A

Sometimes you are asked to fill in the regions of the Venn diagram with the actual elements in a set:

U = {positive integers less than 10}
A= {integers that are multiples of 3}
B = {integers that are factors of 30}
List the elements of A and B and place them in the appropriate region in the Venn diagram. *(Some of this has been done for you).*

A = {......, ..., ...}   B = {......, ..., ..., ..., ...}

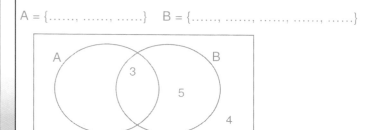

3, 6, 9; 1, 2, 3, 5, 6

A group of 30 children are asked which of the three sports football (F), baseball (B) or volleyball (V) they play. The results are as follows:

2 children do not play any of these sports
3 children play all three sports
4 play volleyball and baseball
8 play football and baseball
7 play football and volleyball
16 play baseball
14 play volleyball

a) **Draw a Venn diagram to illustrate the relationship between the three sports played.**
b) **On your Venn diagram indicate the number of children that belong to each region.**
c) **How many children play only football?**

a) The Venn diagram consists of 3 intersecting circles, each labelled, and inside a rectangle.

b) Start by filling in the 2 who do not play sports – they go outside the circles. This leaves a total of 28 to be filled in inside the circles. Do we know the very centre, the intersection of all 3 sports? – yes, there are 3 children there. These 3 are *included* in the 4 who play volleyball and baseball, so we can fill in a 1 for the rest of the intersection of these two. Then do the same for the remaining intersections.

Now there are 16 who play baseball – including the 9 we already have. So 7 play *only* baseball. Similarly for volleyball. The total inside the circles is now 26, and we are expecting 28. The remaining region (only football) must therefore be 2.

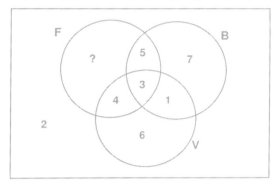

You should draw the Venn diagram for yourself and try filling it in.

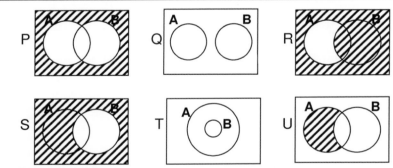

a) **Ignoring the shading, which of the diagrams illustrates**
   i) $A \cup B = A$; (ii) $A \cap B = \varnothing$
b) **In which Venn diagram does the shading represent**
   i)   the complement of B;   (ii) the complement of $A \cup B$?

T, Q, S, P

Analogy between sets and logic: Set notation (eg: A', ∩, ∪) and logic notation (¬a, ∧, ∨) are very close to each other, and Venn diagrams can be used to illustrate logic. For example, if we draw a Venn diagram where set A represents multiples of 3, then the circle can also represent the proposition a: "x is a multiple of 3" with true values inside the circle, false values outside.

Probability Notation and Formulae

Notation: The *sample space* in a given situation is the set of all the things that can happen and is defined by the letter U. An *event* is one of the things that can happen and is given any other capital letter. A capital P stands for "probability", so we can shorten "the probability of event A" to P(A). The number of ways A can happen is denoted by $n(A)$. Probabilities are always numbers between 0 (definitely won't happen) and 1 (definitely will happen).

In other words, to find the probability of an event, divide the number of ways it can (or did) happen by the total number of possibilities.

- $P(A) = \dfrac{n(A)}{n(U)}$

The probability that event *A* does *not* happen is denoted by *A'*. It follows that

- P(A) + P(A') = 1

The set notation symbols ∩ and ∪ are used for the words "and" and "or" in probability.

A basket of fruit contains 10 apples, 6 bananas and 4 oranges. A fruit is selected at random.

a)   Find the probability that a fruit selected is not an orange.

There are 20 fruits of which 16 are not oranges so **P(not an orange) = 16/20 = 0.8**

b)   The first and second fruits selected are both bananas and they are eaten. Find the probability that the next fruit selected will be an apple.

There are now 18 fruits left of which 10 are still apples. So **P(apple) = 10/18**

Combined events: The probability of event *A or* event *B* happening (and this includes both) is calculated using addition.

- P(A∪B)=P(A)+P(B)

but this formula works **only** if A and B are *mutually exclusive* – ie they cannot both happen at the same time. If they are not mutually exclusive, use:

- P(A∪B)=P(A)+P(B)-P(A∩B)

The probability of events A and B *both* happening is calculated by multiplication (remember that multiplying fractions gives a *smaller* answer and it is *less* likely that both events will happen than just one).

- P(A∩B)=P(A)×P(B)

A bag contains balls of two different colours. One is taken out, then another. The colour of the second is independent of the first if the first has been put back. If the first has been kept out, the colour of the second *depends* on the colour of the first.

but this formula works **only** if A and B are *independent* – ie one of them happening does not affect the probability of the other happening. If the events are not independent we are into the realms of *conditional probability* – ie the probability of one event happening if another has already happened. This is written as P(A|B), and read as "the probability of A given B."

The formulae can be quite difficult to use, so only use them if you *have* to. Many probability questions can be solved by using appropriate diagrams as shown on the next few pages.

Carlos travels each day by bicycle (probability 0.25), train (probability 0.65) or car. Find the probability that he travels

a)   by car on any day

b)   by bicycle on Thursday and Friday *("and" is multiply)*

c)   by bicycle on Monday and by train on Thursday

d)   either by train or by car on Monday and Tuesday. *(Consider "train or car" as a single event – what is its probability?)*

e)   by the same method of travel on Wednesday and Thursday. *(ie car and car or train and train or bicycle and bicycle).*   0.1,   0.0625,   0.1625,   0.5625,   0.495

Lists and Tables of Outcomes

Lists: A list of possible outcomes is useful if there aren't too many of them. And it is important to ensure that each outcome in the list is equally likely. For example, when three coins are thrown, the possible combinations of heads and tails are:

HHH, HHT, HTH, HTT, THH, THT, TTH, TTT

If we want to find P(exactly two heads) we can see that there are three ways of achieving this (HHT, HTH, THH) so the probability is 3/8.

Five cards (numbered 1 to 5) are shuffled and two selected at random, one after the other.
a)   What is the probability that the number on the first card selected is larger than the number on the second card?
b)   What is the probability that the sum of the two numbers is divisible by 3?

There are few enough combinations to make it worthwhile listing *all* the possibilities.

12, 13, 14, 15, 21, 23, 24, 25, 31, 32, 34, 35, 41, 42, 43, 45, 51, 52, 53, 54

(The first card is *not* replaced, so 22 for example is not a possibility. And order matters, so 21 is different from 12).

a)   There are 20 combinations. 10 of them have the first number larger than the second.
        So probability = **10/20** (which can be deduced from common sense)!

b)   The following combinations are divisible by 3: 12, 15, 21, 24, 42, 45, 51, 54, so
        probability = **8/20**

Tables of outcomes: Tables of outcomes show how many ways two events can, or cannot, happen.

In a survey of 48 students it was found that 30 study Spanish and 13 study Maths. Six of those who study Spanish also study Maths.
a)   Copy and complete the table.

The 30 and the 13 will be totals, the 6 goes in the "study Spanish, study Maths box" – then the rest can be completed.

	Study Spanish	Do not study Spanish	Total
Study Maths	6	7	13
Do not study Maths	24	11	35
Total	30	18	48

b)   What is the probability that a student selected at random:
i)   studies Maths and studies Spanish?
ii)   studies Maths but does not study Spanish?
iii)   studies Maths if he studies Spanish?

i)   This applies to 6 students, so probability = **6/48**
ii)   This applies to 7 students, so probability = **7/48**

iii)   This is a conditional probability, but we do not need to use the formula. We *know* that the student studies Spanish and so is one of 30. Of these 30, 6 study Maths. Therefore, the probability = **6/30**

Use of Diagrams

Room

```
Black Hair    Glasses

    9     2     4

5
```

Venn diagrams: Venn Diagrams were introduced on page 30. They can be an extremely useful tool when solving probability questions. Take the example on page 30 where 20 people are in a room, some with black hair and some with glasses.

Once the data has been entered into the diagram, all probabilities associated with it can be easily calculated. When someone is selected at random, the probability they have:

Black hair and glasses = 2/20
Black hair and no glasses = 9/20
Not got glasses = 14/20
Glasses or black hair (or both) = 15/20
Either glasses or black hair = 13/20

The symbol for the probability of A given B is P(A|B). There is a formula for this:

$$P(A|B) = \frac{P(A \cap B)}{P(B)}$$

but you will usually use diagrams, such as Venn diagrams, for any calculations.

Conditional probability: Suppose someone is selected at random and we are told that they have black hair. What is the probability that they have glasses? In this situation we have extra knowledge, and this changes the probability. There are 11 people with black hair, so the selected person must be one of those; and of those 11, only 2 have glasses, so the probability is 2/11. This is known as *conditional probability*, and often uses the words "given that".

P(someone has glasses given that they have black hair) = 2/11

9/14

What will be the probability that the selected person has black hair given that they do not have glasses?

The Venn diagram shows the number of students in a year group at a school who have joined creative clubs. **A** is those who do Art, **M** is those who do Music, **P** is those who do Photography.

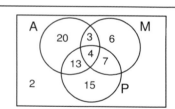

a) How many are there in the year group?

b) If a student is chosen at random, what is the probability that they:
  - **i)** do Music;
  - **ii)** do Art and Photography;
  - **ii)** have not joined a creative club?

c) What is the probability that an artist is also a musician?

a) Adding up all the numbers gives **70**.
b) i) 20 do music altogether, so P(music) = **20/70**
    ii) There are 17 in the intersection of A and P, so P(art and photography) = **17/70**
    iii) There are 2 in the outer region, so P(have not joined any club) = **2/70**
c) This is conditional probability: we *know* that the person chosen is an artist. There are 40 in the art club altogether, and 7 of these are musicians. So P(M|A) = **7/40**

You may well have to complete the Venn diagram first, and then use it to calculate probabilities. Use the bulleted points on page 30 to help you complete the Venn diagram in the question over the page. Note that the last part of the question has a "given that" in it.

A survey of 100 school children was carried out, asking about the pets they had at home. The results were:

    14 owned birds (B)
    31 owned cats (C)
    50 owned dogs (D)
    3 owned birds and cats, but not dogs
    4 owned birds and dogs, but not cats
    14 owned cats and dogs, but not birds
    2 owned all three types

a) Draw a Venn diagram to represent this information
   (Make it a good size so you can show the information clearly).
b) How many children own no pets?
c) What is the probability that a child has exactly two pets?
d) A child is chosen at random. What is the probability that they own a bird, given that they own a dog?

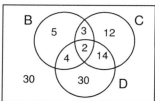

(b) **30**   (c) **0.21**   (d) **0.12**

Tree diagrams: Tree diagrams are used to work out the probabilities for a *succession* of events. To find the probability of a set of successive branches, multiply each individual probability. To find the probability of one of several branches occurring, add the probabilities of each outcome.

Note that the probabilities associated with, say, taking two balls out of a bag simultaneously are the same as if the balls were taken out consecutively.

eg: P*(rains today)* = 0.3.
If it rains today, P*(rains tomorrow)* = 0.65. However, if it is dry today, P*(rains tomorrow)* = 0.2.

The tree diagram on the right shows the full set of possible outcomes and their associated probabilities.

Note the following points:
- Probabilities of branches coming out of one point add to give 1 since they cover all possibilities.
- The overall probabilities also add to give 1.
- The weather tomorrow is *not* independent of the weather today, hence the different probabilities depending on today's weather.

Today

Tomorrow

0.3 Rain
0.65 Rain **0.195**
0.35 Dry **0.105**

0.7 Dry
0.2 Rain **0.14**
0.8 Dry **0.56**

Some example probabilities are:
- P(two rainy days) = 0.195
- P(at least one rainy day) = 0.195 + 0.105 + 0.14 = 0.44
- P(exactly one rainy day) = 0.105 + 0.14 = 0.245

In the senior class there are 20 boys and 26 girls.
a) One student is selected randomly. What is the probability that a girl is selected? *How many students altogether? How many of them are girls?*

b) Two students are selected randomly to meet the school inspector. What is the probability that they are both of the same sex? *Draw a tree diagram which shows the four possible combinations. When putting the probabilities on the second set of branches, remember that one student has already been selected.*

(a) **26/46**   (b) **103/207 or 0.498**

With and without replacement: In the question on the previous page, the probability of choosing two boys in part (b) is $\frac{20}{46} \times \frac{19}{45}$.

This is because if a boy has been chosen first, there are then 19 boys left out of 45 students. Similarly, the P(two girls) = $\frac{26}{46} \times \frac{25}{45}$.

The principle here is called "without replacement" since the first person chosen is not replaced in the group, and cannot be chosen again. In some questions you must read the question carefully to decide whether to use "with replacement" or "without replacement."

---

a) A bag contains 6 green apples and 10 red apples. Without looking into the bag, Mary randomly selects one apple. What is the probability that it is green?

6/16

b) The apple is green and Mary eats it. The bag is passed to Oliver who randomly selects an apple – what is the probability that it is red?

10/15

c) The apple is red and Oliver replaces it in the bag. Now the bag is passed to Peter who randomly selects two apples. What is the probability they are both green?

2/21

Mark wakes up late on work days 1 day in 5. If he wakes up late, the probability he misses his bus is 0.8, otherwise it is 0.1.

Complete the tree diagram to represent this information.

a)   What is the probability that he misses the bus on a work day?
b)   Over a period of 50 work days, on how many days would Mark be expected to catch the bus.

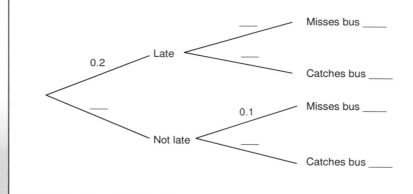

(a) 0.24 (b) 38

Sample space diagrams: A diagram where each possibility is represented by a dot is called a *sample space diagram*. It is particularly useful for recording the possible outcomes when two events occur simultaneously. Probabilities can then be found by circling the dots which represent the required outcome, and dividing that number by the total number.

Suppose we have a spinner which is divided into four equal sections lettered A, B, E, G. The spinner is spun twice, and the letter it lands on is recorded each time. The sample space diagram on the next page shows all the possible outcomes.

We can see that there are 16 possible outcomes.
Now, work out how many dots represent:
a) Both letters the same.
b) Both letters vowels.
c) Just one letter a vowel.
d) The first letter higher in the alphabet than the second.

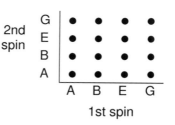

2nd spin

It's important to understand that there are two ways of getting an A and a B, for example (AB or BA), but there is only one way of getting two As.

To work out the probability of each event, simply put the numbers over 16 (answers on the right).

$$\frac{4}{16}, \frac{4}{16}, \frac{8}{16}, \frac{6}{16}$$

Sample space diagrams can be used to calculate conditional probabilities as well. The diagram below shows the totals when two four-sided dice are rolled – I've put the actual totals in, but dots would be just as good.

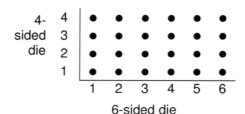

1st die

$$P(\text{total is at least 5}) = \frac{10}{16} \text{ (see shaded area). But, suppose we are}$$

given that the total is at least 5, we could count the outcomes to work out probabilities such as:

$$P(\text{total} < 7 \text{ given that total is at least 5}) = \frac{7}{10}$$

$$P(\text{1st die number} > \text{2nd die number} \mid \text{total is at least 5}) = \frac{4}{10}$$

The diagram shows the possible outcomes when a fair six-sided die and a fair four-sided die are both rolled together.

4-sided die

6-sided die

a)   **Find the probability that the two dice show the same number.**
b)   **Find the probability that the numbers on the two dice differ by exactly 2.**
c)   **Given that the two dice show the same number, find the probability that the total is greater than 6.**
d)   **Given that the total is greater than 6, find the probability that the two dice show the same number.**

$$\frac{4}{24}, \frac{6}{24}, \frac{1}{4}, \frac{1}{10}$$

The Normal Distribution

Suppose we took a random sample of 1000 people, measured their heights to the nearest cm, and plotted a frequency histogram showing the number of people for each height. The *distribution* would look very like the diagram on the left. Points to note:

- The bars would be so close together that they effectively form a smooth curve
- The diagram is completely symmetrical around the central value which is the mean of the distribution.
- Most heights are clustered close to the mean, with fewer and fewer as you move out to the very short and very tall people.

Examples:
- *Weights of people*
- *Lifetimes of elephants*
- *IQs of schoolchildren*
- *Sale prices of houses in a given area*

The distribution is called *normal* and many naturally occurring random variables will be normally distributed. In each case, the mean (μ) and the standard deviation (σ) will be different, but the shape will be the same. The standard deviation will define the range of results, and you should remember that:

- 68% of the data lies within ± 1 standard deviation of the mean;
- 95% of the data lies within ± 2 standard deviations of the mean;
- 99% of the data (so pretty well all of it) lies within ± 3 standard deviations of the mean.

Calculating probabilities: The normal distribution is a *probability distribution* which means that we can use the area under the curve to find the probability that the variable lies between two values. Suppose the mean height of the 1000 people mentioned above is 175cm, with standard deviation 6cm. How can we find the probability that someone chosen at random has a height between 172cm and 180cm? The sketch on the left shows the normal curve with a mean of 175cm, and the relevant area shaded.

175

Each division on the x-axis is 1 standard deviation.

Fortunately, your GDC will do the hard work for you. You will need to enter the lower and upper values, μ and σ, and out pops the answer 0.489. Another interpretation is that just over 25% of the group have heights within this range.

To calculate P(height > 180cm) you will use 176 as the lower value, and it is conventional to enter something like 10^{99} as the upper value – but any large value will do. Your answer should be 0.202.

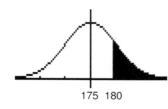

175 180

Note that, since you can't back up your GDC answers with working, you should always draw sketches such as those on the left when answering exam questions – a sketch will show that you understand the theory behind the calculation.

Expected values: Suppose we took 50 people from the group of 1000: how many of these would we expect to have a height greater than 180cm? Since P(height > 180cm) = 0.202, the *expected value* would be 0.202 × 50 = 10.1. We would therefore expect 10 people to be over 180cm.

A machine tool manufactures components whose weight is normally distributed with mean 85g and standard deviation 0.4g.

a) **Explain why you would not expect a component to be manufactured weighing 87g.**
$\mu + 3\sigma = 85 + 3 \times 0.4 = 86.2$. 87g is therefore significantly beyond 3 standard deviations from the mean, and hence very unlikely to occur.

b) **Find the probability that a component weighs less than 84.5g.**
From the GDC, P(weight < 84.5g) = **0.106**

c) **100 components are chosen at random. How many would be expected to weigh more than 84.5g.**
We would expect 0.106 × 100 = 11 to weigh less than 84.5g. Therefore, the expected value weighing more than 84.5g = 100 − 11 = **89**

84.5   85

Inverse normal calculations: Using the inverse normal function on the GDC we can turn the probability calculations around: given a probability we can find the value associated with that probability. For example, we are told that the weights of potatoes in a particular crop are normally distributed with mean 120g and standard deviation 15g. The lightest 12% of the crop is to be categorised as "small": what is the maximum weight of a small potato?

We can answer this by noting that the probability of a potato being small is 0.12. Now use the inverse normal function with this probability, and with μ = 120 and σ = 15, to get the "cut off" point for small potatoes as 102.4g.

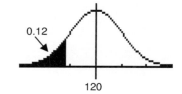

Be careful if you are dealing with the upper end of the distribution because the calculations always use areas starting at the lower end. So, if we are told that 8% of potatoes are to be classified as "large", we will enter 0.92 into the GDC (see the lower diagram on the right). Try this, and you should find that large potatoes will weigh at least 141g.

The IQ scores of a group of 120 students were measured and found to be normally distributed with a mean of 121 and standard deviation 6.

a) What is the probability that a student chosen at random from the group had an IQ score
i)   Greater than 128
ii)   Less than 122
b) How many of the students had IQ scores between 115 and 120?
c) What was the lowest possible IQ score of the top 15% of the group, assuming all the results are given as whole numbers?

(a) 0.122, 0.566.   (b) 33   (c) 128

Further normal probability practice:
A normal probability distribution X has μ = 12.8 and σ = 0.75.
Calculate:
a)   P(12 < x < 13)
b)   P(x > 12.95)
c)   P(Two values chosen at random are both less than 12.5)
d)   The value of X below which only 5% of the distribution lies.

ANSWERS
a) 0.462
b) 0.421
c) 0.119
d) 11.57

Correlation

Scatter diagrams: Two sets of data which appear to have a relationship between them are said to be *correlated*. For example, a company may find that there is a direct relationship between the amount it spends on advertising and its sales figures. Note that correlation does not imply causality: the correlation may be coincidental, or it may be linked to a third factor (perhaps, in this case, differing economic conditions). A simple way to assess possible correlation is to draw a *scatter diagram*. The two sets of data are plotted on a standard *x-y graph* (but not joined in any way). Qualitative conclusions which can be drawn about the correlation are:

It is not necessary for the axes in a scatter diagram to be labelled from 0. We are only interested in the relationship between the points.

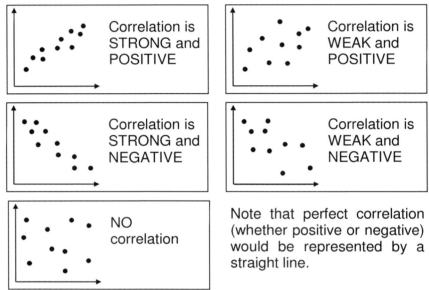

Correlation is STRONG and POSITIVE

Correlation is WEAK and POSITIVE

Correlation is STRONG and NEGATIVE

Correlation is WEAK and NEGATIVE

NO correlation

Note that perfect correlation (whether positive or negative) would be represented by a straight line.

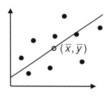

Line of best fit: A scatter diagram indicates the relationship between two variables. If we conclude that there *is* a relationship, we can draw in the "line of best fit" by eye and then use this to predict more pairs of values. If you know the mean values of the two variables, the line of best fit should pass through the point $(\bar{x}, \bar{y})$. Note that although *interpolation* (ie putting new points in between existing points) is fairly safe, *extrapolation* (ie continuing the line beyond the existing points) may not be valid. There may be reasons why the relationship does not continue in the same way.

Correlation Coefficient: For a quantitative assessment of correlation we can calculate the *product-moment* coefficient, denoted by r. This is derived from all the pairs of values such that:
- A coefficient of -1 indicates perfect negative correlation.
- A coefficient of 0 indicates no correlation.
- A coefficient of +1 indicates perfect positive correlation.

The size of r (ie the positive value of r) indicates the strength of the correlation, but this also depends on the number of pairs of values. However, we can say generally that:
- $0.25 \leq r < 0.5 \Rightarrow$ weak correlation
- $0.5 \leq r < 0.75 \Rightarrow$ moderate correlation
- $0.75 \leq r < 1 \Rightarrow$ strong correlation

(and similarly for negative values of r).

Calculating the coefficient: You may have been using the formula for calculating the correlation coefficient, but you will not have to do this in the exam. However, you *are* expected to be able to use your GDC to find the correlation coefficient given the raw data. ▤ Since different calculators work in different ways, no steps are given here. But, whichever calculator you use, you must be able to enter two sets of data and then access the relevant calculations.

The table shows the blood pressure as measured for 9 people of varying ages.

Age	19	35	51	24	58	45	27	33	69
Blood pressure	55	60	80	65	75	85	70	75	85

Calculate the product-moment correlation coefficient and hence comment on the statement that "blood pressure increase with age."

$r = 0.783$ There is strong evidence to suggest blood pressure increases with age.

Regression lines: The line of best fit on a scatter diagram is called a "regression line" and it can be calculated from the data pairs. Again, you will not be required to use the formula in the exam, but you must be able to use your GDC to find the regression line.

In a study of a city, the population density (y) was compared to the distance from the city centre (x) for a number of sample areas. The results were:

x	0.6	3.8	2.4	3.0	2.0	1.5	1.8	3.4	4.0	0.9
y	50	22	14	20	33	47	25	8	16	38

a) Draw a scattergraph and find the equation of the regression line.
b) Use your formula to predict the population density 2.2km from the centre.
c) Why could the regression line not be used to predict the population density 6km from the centre?

a) After entering the data into the GDC, the formula for the regression line is found to be
$$y = -9.85x + 50.3$$

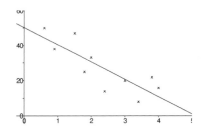

b) Substituting $x = 2.2$ into the formula gives $y = 28.6$.

c) The relationship cannot continue beyond about 5km because it would give negative values for population density.

It is expected that the yield y of a crop, in kg/unit area, is related to the amount of fertiliser, x kg used per unit area. The table shows observed yields for various values of x.

x	10	2	11	3	15	5	6	21	8	13
y	39	20	48	20	56	29	36	70	44	59

a) Write down the mean and standard deviation of the values for the yield.
b) Write down the correlation coefficient, r, for the data, and comment on its value.
c) Write down the equation of the regression line of y on x.
d) Using your equation, determine the expected yield if 18g of fertiliser were to be used.
e) A farmer wants to use the equation to determine how much fertiliser to use to create a yield of 100 kg/unit area. Why would you advise against this?

(a) 42.1, 15.78 (b) 0.967, strong positive correlation (c) $y = 2.74x + 16.34$
(d) 65.66kg/unit area (e) He would be extrapolating beyond the observed values

The χ^2 Test

Contingency Tables: A contingency table is a sort of Venn diagram which shows how a population splits according to two factors. We would like to see whether or not the two factors are independent of each other. The procedure is to take a table of observed frequencies and, from this, draw up a table of *expected* frequencies on the assumption of independence. For example, suppose we take a group of 80 people split into 3 age groups, and we are interested to see how many of each have gained penalty points on their driving licence during the last year.

	Age < 21	21 ≤ Age ≤ 60	Age > 60	Total
No points	24	19	21	64
Points	10	1	5	16
Total	34	20	26	80

Working out the expected frequencies: We can see that one-fifth of the group gained points: we would therefore expect, for example, 4 of the middle age group to have gained points . 4 is the *expected* frequency, and the calculation to work it out is $\dfrac{16 \times 20}{80}$;

in general, the calculation is $\dfrac{\text{row total} \times \text{column total}}{\text{grand total}}$. (Note that the numbers do not necessarily come out as integers). The table of expected frequencies is calculated as:

The newly calculated figures are shown in bold

	Age < 21	21 ≤ Age ≤ 60	Age > 60	Total
No points	**27**	**16**	**21**	64
Points	**7**	**4**	**5**	16
Total	34	20	26	80

So the number of under 21's with penalty points is more than we expected – could it be this high by chance alone, or could it be that the two factors (age and points) are in fact related?

χ^2 test: We now need a statistic which measures by how much the observed frequencies differ from the expected frequencies. This is called the χ^2 statistic; the higher it is, the further the observed values deviate from the expected values, and so the less likely that chance alone is involved. In the exam you will need to be able to enter the observed frequencies into your GDC, and then use the stats functions to calculate the statistic. In this case, $\chi^2 = 4.7$

Find out how to enter the observed frequencies into your GDC. It can then calculate the expected frequencies and the value of χ^2.

On its own, this doesn't tell us much. We now need a *critical value* for χ^2 which tells us at which point "could have happened by chance" becomes "unlikely to have happened by chance." This critical value depends on the number of *degrees of freedom* and also on the *significance level* we set for the test.

Degrees of freedom: The more rows and columns we have, the more pairs of values there will be. So the value of χ^2 will be higher, and so will the critical value. The number of "degrees of freedom" is calculated as (rows − 1) × (columns − 1); in our example, this is $(2 − 1)(3 − 1) = 2$. The term degrees of freedom does not need to be understood, but you must be able to calculate it!

Significance level: How certain do we want to be that the value of χ^2 could not happen by chance alone? A significance level of 5% means that only in 5% of cases would you get a value this high or higher. This in turn means that if our value of χ^2 is above the critical value, we can be at least 95% certain that the things we are measuring *are* in fact related. If we want to be at least 99% certain, we go for a significance level of 1%.

The test: In the exam you will be given the critical value. In our case, for 2 degrees of freedom, the critical value is 4.605 at the 10% level, 5.991 at the 5% level and 7.378 at the 1% level. So, if we had set the level at 5%, $\chi^2 = 4.7$ is *not* significant, and the observed frequencies could have happened by chance. There is no evidence to suggest that age and penalty points are related.

...but at the 10% level, a less stringent test, the result is significant, and we could say that the number of points is related to age.

Hypothesis testing: All of the above can be bundled up into a *hypothesis test*, and you should always write these out in the same way. We begin with a *null hypothesis* (that the quantities are independent) and an *alternative hypothesis* (that they are not independent). These are written as H_0 and H_1. Let's see how to write out the complete test:

> H_0: Penalty points are independent of age
> H_1: Penalty points are not independent of age
>
> Significance level = 5%
>
> $\chi^2 = 4.7$
>
> Degrees of freedom = 2
>
> Critical value = 5.991
>
> $4.7 < 5.991 \Rightarrow$ accept H_0
>
> Conclusion: There is no evidence to suggest that the number of penalty points depends on age.

200 people from different areas in a country were asked which was their preferred radio station. The results are shown in the table below:

	Radio X	Radio Y	Radio Z	TOTALS
North	42	13	35	90
Central	30	10	20	60
South	13	17	20	50
TOTALS	85	40	75	200

A chi-squared test for independence is to be carried out at the 5% level.
a) Write down the null and alternative hypotheses.
b) What is the expected number of Radio Y listeners in the Central area?
c) Write down the χ^2 value.
d) Given a critical value of 9.488, state whether you would accept or reject the null hypothesis.
e) In terms of the 5% level, what conclusion do you draw?

(You will find the answers to this question over the page)

For the previous question:
a) H_0: Preferred radio station is independent of where people live
    H_1: Preferred radio station is not independent of where people live
b) 12

c) 11.39

d) 11.39 > 9.488, therefore reject H_0

e) The evidence suggests that people living in different areas prefer different radio stations. The probability of the observed frequencies happening by chance alone is less than 5%.

p-value: For a particular value of χ^2, and with a particular number of degrees of freedom, the p-value measures the probability that the test statistic is at least as high as the one actually obtained. For the question above, the p-value is 0.0225. Put simply, the lower the p-value, the more extreme the statistic, and therefore the more likely that the quantities being measured are not independent.

Further practice:

A certain type of electronic component is made in three different factories. Samples were taken from each to see how many were defective. Fill in the totals in the contingency table below which shows the results of the sampling:

	Satisfactory	Defective	Totals
Factory A	97	3	
Factory B	65	5	
Factory C	65	15	
Totals			

a) What is the probability that a component chosen at random:
   i)   Came from Factory B?
   ii)   Was a defective from Factory C?
   iii) Was satisfactory given that it came from Factory A?

b) Complete the table below with all the expected frequencies, giving answers to the nearest whole number.

Because of rounding areas, you may find that the totals don't add exactly to give the grand total.

	Satisfactory	Defective	Totals
Factory A		9	
Factory B			
Factory C	73		
Totals	227		250

A chi-squared test is carried out to see if the proportion of defective components is different at each factory.

c) Write down the null hypothesis.

d) Write down the χ^2 statistic.

e) Write down the number of degrees of freedom.

f) At the 1% level, the critical value is 9.21. The p-value is 0.001 What conclusions can be drawn?

ANSWERS

Row totals: 100, 70, 80; Column totals: 227, 23; Grand total: 250.

a)   (i) 0.28; (ii) 0.06; (iii) 0.97.

b)   A/Satis: 91; B/Satis: 64; B/Defect: 6; C/Defect: 7.

c) H_0: The number of defectives is independent of the factory.

d)   13.7

e)   2

f)   Reject H_0. There is quite strong evidence to suggest that some factories produce more defectives than others.

GEOMETRY AND TRIGONOMETRY
Coordinate Geometry

2-D coordinates: In 2 dimensions, we are dealing with the familiar x-y coordinate system: a pair of coordinates such as (2, 5) gives the position of a point compared to the origin (0, 0).

If you can't remember which is x and which is y, remember that the order of the coordinates is "along the corridor, up the stairs" (but not much use if you live in a bungalow).

Formulae
For two points (x_1, y_1) and (x_2, y_2):

Midpoint formula is:
$$\left(\frac{x_1 + x_2}{2}, \frac{y_1 + y_2}{2} \right)$$

Distance between the points is:
$$\sqrt{(x_2 - x_1)^2 + (y_2 - y_1)^2}$$

Gradient is:
$$\frac{y_2 - y_1}{x_2 - x_1}$$

Parallel lines: $m_1 = m_2$
Perpendicular lines:
$m_1 m_2 = -1$

Midpoint of two points:
The x coordinate of the midpoint is halfway between the x coordinates of the two points, and the y coordinate is halfway between the two y coordinates. For example, the midpoint of the line joining (-3, 6) to (5, 2) is (1, 4).

Distance between points: Because a right angled triangle can be formed with the points at two corners, we can use Pythagoras' theorem to calculate the distance. In the example shown right, the x distance between the points is 8 (from −3 to 5) and the y distance is 4 (from 2 to 6): this gives the distance between them as $\sqrt{(4^2 + 8^2)} = \sqrt{80}$.

Gradient: The *gradient* of the line is its "steepness." A gradient of 3 means that y is increasing 3 times faster than x. The gradient is calculated by choosing two points and dividing the change in y by the change in x.

Horizontal lines have gradient 0. Vertical lines have an infinite gradient. Lines angled from bottom left to top right have positive gradients, others have negative gradients.

If two lines have gradients m_1 and m_2 then they are parallel if the gradients are equal, perpendicular if $m_1 m_2 = -1$.

Formulae: The various formulae are shown above. They are very similar and so can be quite confusing. It is often better to draw a sketch and work from that.

An object moving in a straight line passes through the points (3, 0) and (2, 3). The object also passes through the point (0, a). Calculate the value of a.
First of all, a rough diagram helps us to see what is happening.
One way to do this problem is to consider the gradient of the line.
From (3, 0) to (2, 3) is back 1, up 3. This pattern will continue
up the line. The next point will be back 1, up 3, and that takes
us to (1, 6). Do it again, and we get to (0, 9)
So, *$a = 9$*

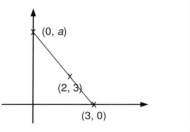

Another way to deal with the question above is to work out the equation of the line (see the next section), and find y when $x = 0$.

Equation of a straight line

When straight lines are drawn on a standard *x-y* grid, the coordinates of every point on the line will satisfy an equation which is called *the equation of the line*.

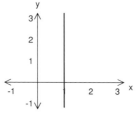

Note that the *equation* of the *x* axis is $y = 0$, and of the *y* axis is $x = 0$.

Vertical and horizontal lines: Lines parallel to the two axes have special equations which you must know. Look at the line on the left. Here are some of the points on it: (1, -1), (1, 0), (1, 3). In every case the *x*-coordinate is 1, so the equation of the line is $x = 1$. All vertical lines have an equation of the form $x = a$, where *a* is any number. Similarly, all horizontal lines have equations of the form $y = a$. If you draw the line $y = 2$ on the same diagram, you will see that the lines intersect at the point (1, 2).

Other lines: All other lines have equations which contain both *x* and *y*: they will either be in the form $ax + by + d = 0$; or they can be in the form $y = mx + c$. Any line can be written in either form, and each has their uses. You should be able to rearrange from one form to the other. For example:

$$2y - 4x + 5 = 0$$
$$2y = 4x - 5$$
$$y = 2x - 2.5$$

The form $y = mx + c$ is particularly useful because *m* will be the gradient of the line, and *c* the point where the line crosses the *y*-axis (known as the *y intercept*). Thus the line above has gradient 2 and cuts the *y*-axis at the point (0, 2.5). Using the formulae on the previous page, this enables us to tell whether two lines are perpendicular or parallel to each other.

The three lines L_1, L_2 and L_3 have the following equations:
$$L_1: y + 3x - 1 = 0; \quad L_2: 3y - x - 2 = 0; \quad L_3: y - 3x + 2 = 0$$

By writing each in the form $y = mx + c$, determine which pairs of lines, if any, are:
  i)   Parallel
  ii)   Perpendicular

If you rearrange each of the equations you should end up with:
$L_1: y = -3x + 1; \quad L_2: y = \frac{1}{3}x + \frac{2}{3}; \quad L_3: y = 3x - 2$. The gradients of these lines are -3, $\frac{1}{3}$, and 3. Parallel lines have the same gradient, the gradients of perpendicular lines multiply to give -1.

Thus: (i) **None of the lines are parallel.** (ii) L_1 and L_2 **are perpendicular.**

Finding the equation of a line: Given any two points on a line, it is always possible to then find its equation. The easiest way is to first find the gradient, and then the intercept, and hence the equation in the form $y = mx + c$.

It's usually helpful to draw a very rough sketch – at least this gives an indication of whether the gradient is –ve or +ve.

Example 1:
Find the equation of the line passing through (2, 4) and (0, 8).

- The gradient of the line $= \dfrac{8 - 4}{0 - 2} = -2$

- Thus the equation of the line is of the form $y = -2x + c$
- The point (0, 8) is the *y*-intercept, so $c = 8$
- So, the equation of the line is $y = -2x + 8$

Alternative forms: $y + 2x = 8$, $y + 2x - 8 = 0$

<u>Example 2:</u>
Find the equation of the line passing through (2, 4) and (4, 9).

This time the sketch shows us that both the gradient and the intercept we calculated look reasonable.

- The gradient of the line = $\dfrac{9-4}{4-2}$ = 2.5
- Thus the equation of the line is of the form $y = 2.5x + c$
- We do not know the intercept, but we can substitute either point into the partial equation. Substituting (2, 4), we get:

$$4 = 2.5 \times 2 + c$$
$$4 = 5 + c$$
$$c = -1$$

- So, the equation of the line is $y = 2.5x - 1$
  Alternative forms: $2y - 5x = -2$, $2y - 5x + 2 = 0$

The coordinates of the vertices of the triangle PQR are P(3, 2), Q(0, 8), R(1, s).
a) Calculate the gradient of the line PQ.
b) Given that line PR is perpendicular to line PQ,
   i) write down the gradient of line PR;
   ii) find the value of p.
For the last part, we need to know the equation of line PR, because we can then substitute the x-coordinate of point R to find the value of s.

(a) -2;   (b)(i) $\frac{1}{2}$ (ii) s = 1.5

Intersection of lines: If two lines intersect, and we know their equations, we can find the point where they intersect. The easiest way to do this is to solve the two equations simultaneously; the solutions for x and y will form the coordinates of the point of intersection. And the easiest way to solve the equations is to ensure they are in the form $ax + by = c$, and then use the simultaneous equation solver on your GDC.

Find the point of intersection of the lines with equations $y = 2x - 3$ and $3x - 2y - 2 = 0$
Start by rearranging both equations in the form ax + by = c.

(4, 5)

Further practice with straight line equations:

1.   Work out the gradients of the following lines:
       $y = 2x - 4$; $y = 3 - x$; $2y - 2x + 1 = 0$; $3y + 2x - 1 = 0$

2.   Write down the gradients of lines which are perpendicular to each of the lines in question 1.

3.   Find the equations of the lines through the following pairs of points: (0, 1) and (5, 2); (-1, -1) and (3, 7); (-2, 1) and (-2, 6).

4.   Find the point of intersection of the lines:
       $y + 2x = 5$ and $4x + y - 3 = 0$

5.   Find the equation of the line through the point (1, -1) which is parallel to the line $2x + 3y - 1 = 0$. Give your answer in the form $ax + by + d = 0$.

ANSWERS
1.   2, -1, 1, $-\frac{2}{3}$
2. $-\frac{1}{2}$, 1, -1, $\frac{3}{2}$
3. $y = \frac{1}{5}x + 1$, $y = 2x + 1$, $x = -2$
4.   (-1, 7)
5. $2x + 3y = -1$

The vertices of a quadrilateral ABCD are shown in the diagram with A(-3, 1), B(-2, -1), C(2, 1) and D(-1, 2)

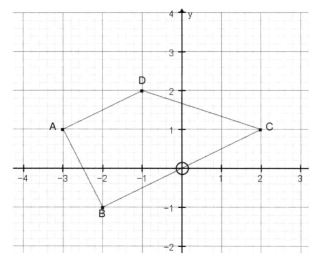

a)   Calculate the gradient of the line AB.
b)   Show that the line AB is perpendicular to the line AD.
c)   Find the equation of the line AB. Give your answer in the form *ax + by = c*, where *a, b, c* are integers.

The equation of line CD is *x* + 3*y* = 5

d)   Show that the coordinates of D satisfy this equation.

Lines AB and CD intersect at the point E.

e)   Find the coordinates of E.
f)   Find the midpoint of BE.
g)   Find the distance from B to C.
h)   Prove that the distance from B to E is $\sqrt{20}$.
i)   Use your answers to parts (g) and (h) to find the area of triangle BCE.
        Why is triangle BCE right-angled? Use the appropriate area formula.

(a) -2 (b) Gradient AD = $\frac{1}{2}$, $-2 \times \frac{1}{2} = -1$ (c) 2*x* + *y* = -5 (d) -1 + 3 ×2 = 5

(e) (-4, 3) (f) (-3, 1) (g) $\sqrt{20}$ (h) Distance = $\sqrt{(-2)^2 + 4^2} = \sqrt{20}$ (i) 10

Solution of Triangles

Right-angled triangles: This page is a reminder of how to deal with the sides and angles of a right-angled triangle. The following page deals with non right-angled triangles.

Pythagoras' Theorem: If you know two sides of a right-angled triangle, you can calculate the third using Pythagoras' Theorem. This states that the square of the hypotenuse (the longest side) equals the sum of the squares of the two shorter sides. As applied to the triangle on the right, $c^2 = a^2 + b^2$. You must remember to subtract if you already have the hypotenuse (it's always opposite the right angle) and want to calculate one of the other sides. For example, $b^2 = c^2 - a^2$.

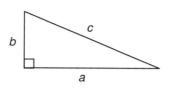

Trigonometry: There is no mystery to sin, cos and tan. They simply represent the ratios of pairs of sides for a triangle with given angles. For example, suppose the smallest angle in the triangle above right is 30°. Whatever the *size* of the triangle, *b* turns out to be half of *c*. The ratio of *b* to *c* is called the sine (sin for short), so sin30° = 0.5. The ratio of *a* to *c* is called the cosine (cos), and *b* to *a* is the tangent (tan). If you use the following procedure *in all cases* then every question can be worked out in the same way, and you should always get the right answer.

1.   Label the three sides of the triangle with H (for hypotenuse, the side opposite the right angle), O (for opposite, the side opposite the angle you are dealing with) and A (for adjacent, the side next to the angle).
2.   For the two sides you are dealing with, write down the word sin, cos or tan according to the mnemonic SOH/CAH/TOA.
3.   Now write down the angle (which may be unknown) followed by an equals sign.
4.   On the right hand side of the equals sign, you will write down a fraction (O over H, A over H or O over A) which will either involve two known sides, or one known and one unknown side.
5.   You will now have an equation to solve. The three examples below show how to do this.

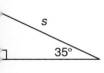

Find *x*.
x is O, 12 is A, so we use tan.
Write down tan, then the angle, then =, then the fraction O/A.
To solve this equation, just multiply through by 12.

$$\tan 72 = \frac{x}{12}$$
$$12 \times \tan 72 = x$$
$$x = 36.9$$

Find *s*.
s is H, 7.5 is O, so we use sin.
Write down sin, then the angle, then =, then the fraction O/H *(note that this time the unknown side will be on the bottom of the fraction)*.
This time, we must "cross-multiply" to solve the equation.

$$\sin 35 = \frac{7.5}{s}$$
$$s = \frac{7.5}{\sin 35}$$
$$s = 13.1$$

Find the angle θ°.
13 is A, 18 is H, so we use cos.
Write down cos, then the angle, then =, then the fraction A/H.
Calculate the value of the fraction, then use the cos⁻¹ function to find out the angle (cos⁻¹ means "find the angle whose cosine is...)

$$\cos \theta = \frac{13}{18}$$
$$\cos \theta = 0.7222$$
$$\theta = \cos^{-1} 0.7222$$
$$\theta = 43.8°$$

⬛ Having worked out 13/18, leave the answer on the display. Then work out the angle using cos⁻¹ANS. This ensures full accuracy.

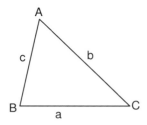

Sine and Cosine Rules: For triangles which are *not* right-angled we use the sine and cosine rules. The triangle on the left has the conventional notation of small letters for the lengths of sides and capital letters for the angles opposite. To find lengths and angles, use:

- The sine rule if 2 sides and 2 angles are involved
- The cosine rule if 3 sides and 1 angle are involved

SINE RULE	COSINE RULE
$\dfrac{a}{\sin A} = \dfrac{b}{\sin B} = \dfrac{c}{\sin C}$	$a^2 = b^2 + c^2 - 2bc\cos A$ *(for a side)* $\cos A = \dfrac{b^2 + c^2 - a^2}{2bc}$ *(for an angle)*

Don't be put off by the letters. Basically, the sine rule says the ratio of side/sine is the same for each pair of sides and angles. And in the cosine rule, ensure that the side on the LHS of the equation matches the angle on the RHS.

In triangle ABC, angle B = 43°, AC = 6.8 cm and AB = 4.3cm. Find the size of angle A, giving your answer to the nearest degree.

It is essential to draw a rough diagram which will show you how to proceed.
We know 2 sides and 1 angle and we want another angle, so we use
the sine rule. We can only find angle C at the moment, using:

$\dfrac{4.3}{\sin C} = \dfrac{6.8}{\sin 43}$ which gives C = 25.55°. So A = 180 − (43+25.55)

A = 111.45° = **111°** to the nearest degree

Town A is 48km from town B and 32km from town C. If B is 56km from town C, find the size of angle CAB to the nearest degree.

Use the cosine rule (in its second form), making sure that the side opposite angle A is also on the left hand side of the formula.

CAB = 86°

Area of a non-right angled triangle: If you know two sides of a triangle, and the size of the angle between the two sides, then the area of the triangle can be found using:

$$\text{Area} = \frac{1}{2}ab\sin C$$

The diagram shows a triangle with sides 5, 7 and 8. Find the size of the smallest angle and the area of the triangle.

The smallest angle is opposite the smallest side, 5.

$\cos x = \dfrac{7^2 + 8^2 - 5^2}{2 \times 7 \times 8} = 0.786$. So the angle is **38.2°**

Area = ½ × 7 × 8 × sin38.2° = **17.3**
(Remember that the angle used in the area formula must be between the two sides used).

Bearings: One of the practical applications of non-right angled trigonometry is the calculation of distances and angles for moving ships and planes. Their direction of travel is based on compass directions, called *bearings*. A bearing is an angle measured around clockwise from North. Always draw in North lines on your diagrams before marking in bearings.

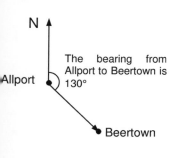

This angle is the bearing

Ship's direction

If a question involves bearings between places, check whether you are dealing with the bearing of A from B or the bearing from A to B, which is the other way round. Use arrows to show in which direction to take the bearing, and put the North line at the *start* of the arrow.

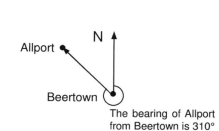

N

Allport

The bearing from Allport to Beertown is 130°

Beertown

N

Allport

Beertown

The bearing of Allport from Beertown is 310°

There is always a difference of 180° between bearings in opposite directions.

A ship sails from port P and travels due South to port Q. From port Q it sails on a bearing of 065° and travels for 45km to a point R, which is due East of P.
a)   i)   Draw and label clearly a diagram to show P, Q and R.
        ii)   Calculate the distance form port P to point R.
In questions like this the diagram is an important tool, so make it large. Angles do not have to be accurate nor lengths drawn to scale, but make them look approximately right.

ii)   Using SOHCAHTOA (because the triangle is right angled) we can see that $\sin 65 = \dfrac{PR}{45} \Rightarrow PR = 45\sin 65 = 40.8$

The distance from P to R is 40.8km

A second ship also sails from port P for 45km to a point S, but on a bearing of 330°.
b)   Complete your diagram in part (a) to show point S.
c)   Calculate the distance from R to S (shown with a grey dotted line) **and the angle PRS.**

Rather than putting in 330°, the more useful 30° has been shown instead. The 40.8 has also been put in: always keep your diagrams up-to-date with new information.

To calculate RS, we use triangle PRS which is not right angled. We already know two sides and one angle (SPR = 30 + 90 = 120°), so we use the cosine rule: $RS^2 = 45^2 + 40.783^2 - 2 \times 45 \times 40.783 \times \cos 120$

$RS = \sqrt{5523.5} = 74.3km$ (Check: RS < RP + PS. Looks OK)

Now we need to calculate angle PRS. We know one angle and two sides so we use the sine rule.

$\dfrac{\sin PRS}{45} = \dfrac{\sin 120}{74.321} \Rightarrow \sin PRS = \dfrac{45\sin 120}{74.321} = 0.5244$

So angle PRS = $\sin^{-1}$(0.5244) = 31.6°

d)   **What is the bearing of S from R?**

The diagram shows the arrow representing S from R, and a new North line inserted. The required bearing has also been put in. How big is this angle? From North round to West is 270°, and then we need another 31.6. So, **the bearing of S from R = 301.6°**

(Note that throughout the question calculations have been performed with numbers to 4 SF accuracy, even if answers are given to 3 SF)

3-D Geometry

You have to be able to combine the rules of 3-D coordinates with the trigonometry of both right angled and non-right angled triangles in order to find the sides and angles of cuboids, prisms and pyramids.

Cuboid: A cuboid is the 3-D equivalent of a rectangle. It has 12 edges, 4 each in three different dimensions (the length, width and height). Commonly asked questions involve the lengths of diagonals (both of sides and also of from one corner to the opposite corner) and angles between various lines. The points used will be the vertices (corners) and the midpoints of sides.

Pyramid: You only have to concern yourself with a "right" pyramid – ie where the apex is directly above the centre of the base, which is itself a square. Pyramid questions almost invariably use the midpoints of sides, and it should be noted that a line drawn from the midpoint of one of the base edges to the apex is at right angles to the base edge.

Prism: A prism is any 3-D shape with the same cross-section throughout its length. Very often this cross-section is a triangle, but it does not have to be.

Angle between a line and a plane: A plane is a flat surface, so each of the faces of the 3-D shapes on the left is a plane. The angle between a line and a plane is the angle between the line and its *projection* on the plane: think of the projection as part of a "shadow line" on the plane.

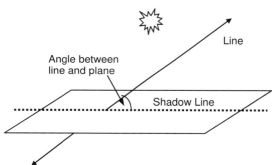

Calculating lengths and angles in 3 dimensions: In every case, you convert the question into an appropriate 2-D question, usually by identifying a right-angled triangle containing the length/angle you have to work out, drawing it as it really looks, then using trigonometry and Pythagoras as usual. For example, the base edges of a pyramid are 10cm and the slant edges are 12cm. M is the midpoint of side PQ and X is the centre point of the base. Find length AM and angle AMX to the nearest degree.

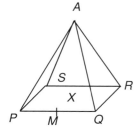

We can find AM using triangle AMQ. MQ = 5 (half of the base length) so $AM^2 = 12^2 - 5^2 \Rightarrow$ AM = $\sqrt{119}$. Now we can draw triangle AMX because we know MX = 5 and AM = $\sqrt{119}$. We can see from the diagram on the left that $\cos AMX = \dfrac{5}{\sqrt{119}} = 0.458$, so angle AMX = 63°,

Here is a complete worked paper 2 question:

An office tower is in the shape of a cuboid with a square base. The roof of the tower is in the shape of a square based right pyramid. The diagram shows some dimensions but is not to scale.

a)   Calculate, correct to 3 significant figures:

  i)   The angle between OF and FG;
  ii)   The shortest distance from O to FG;
  iii)   The total surface area of the four triangular roof sections.
  iv)   The size of the angle between the slant height of the roof and the plane EFGH;
  v)   The height of the tower from the base to O.

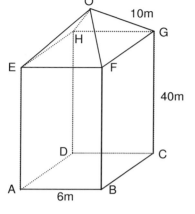

i) Since the pyramid is symmetrical, all the slant heights are 10m. The length FG is 6m because it is the same as AB. We draw triangle OFG, and can use the trigonometry of an isosceles triangle.

$$\cos OFG = \frac{3}{10} = 0.3 \Rightarrow \textbf{OFG = 72.5°}$$

ii)   The shortest distance from O to FG can also be seen in the same triangle – it is the line straight down from O to the midpoint of the base – call it X. We could use trigonometry or Pythagoras. $OX^2 + 3^2 = 10^2 \Rightarrow \textbf{OX} = \sqrt{91}$

iii) Looking at the diagram for triangle OFG, we can see that its base is 6m and its height has just been calculated as $\sqrt{91}$m. So the area of the triangle is $0.5 \times 6 \times \sqrt{91} = 28.62m^2$
So the total area of the roof = $28.62 \times 4 = \textbf{114.5m}^2$

iv)   Imagine the shadow line of OF on the plane EFGH – it is along the line FH. So we need the angle between OF and FH. FH would be a useful length to know: using Pythagoras on triangle FGH we get $FH^2 = 6^2 + 6^2 \Rightarrow FH = \sqrt{72}$. Is there a right angled triangle we could use to find angle OFH? Yes, if we drop a line from O to the centre of the base of the pyramid: call this point P. FP is half the diagonal FH ie $0.5 \times \sqrt{72}$. Now we can easily calculate OFP

$$\cos OFP = \frac{0.5 \times \sqrt{72}}{10} = 0.424 \Rightarrow \textbf{OFP = 65°}$$

v) The height of the tower will be the height of the cuboid + OP
        Height of tower = $40 + 10\sin 65 = \textbf{49.1m}$

b)   A parrot's nest is perched at a point, P, on the edge of BF of the tower. A person at point A, outside the building, measures the angle of elevation to point P to be 79°. Find, correct to 3 significant figures, the height of the nest from the base of the tower.

We need to draw triangle ABF with the point P marked on it.
Now we can see that the distance we require is BP, and we can use right angled triangle ABP.

$$\tan 79° = \frac{BP}{6} \Rightarrow BP = 6\tan 79° = \textbf{30.9m}$$

Cylinder, Sphere and Cone

Cut along the dotted line and open up to get...

Curved Surface Area: Whilst the concept of the *volume* of shapes with curved edges and faces may not be too difficult to appreciate, the *area* of such curved faces may be problematic. The way to think of such faces is to imagine them to be made from separate pieces of paper; the area of a curved surface is the same as the area of the paper it is made from when it is flattened out. For example, unroll the curved surface of a cylinder and you get a rectangle whose height is the height of the cylinder and whose length is the circumference of the cylinder.

You need to be able to use the relevant area and volume formulae for cylinders, cones and spheres. You will find them all in your list of formulae. They are:

Cylinder: Curved surface area = $2\pi rh$
Volume = $\pi r^2 h$

Cone: Curved surface area = $\pi r l$ (*l* is the slant height)
Volume = $\frac{1}{3}\pi r^2 h$

Sphere: Surface area = $4\pi r^2$
Volume = $\frac{4}{3}\pi r^3$

Read each question very carefully to see *exactly* what you are being asked to find. For example, a cylinder may be completely closed in which case the total surface area is the curved surface area plus the areas of the two ends, which are both circles. Or it may be open at one end, so just add one circle. The volume of a hemisphere is half that of a sphere, but its total surface area will be half the curved surface of a sphere plus the circle which forms its base. Its formula will be $\frac{1}{2}\times 4\pi r^2 + \pi r^2 = 3\pi r^2$.

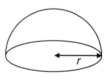

Both a cone and a hemisphere have base diameter of 18cm. If the height of the cone is 10cm, show that the ratio of the volume of the cone to that of the hemisphere is 5:9.

The volume of the cone is $\frac{1}{3}\pi r^2 h = \frac{1}{3}\pi\times 9^2\times 10 = 270\pi$. The volume of the hemisphere is $\frac{1}{2}\times\frac{4}{3}\pi r^3 = \frac{2}{3}\pi\times 9^3 = 486\pi$. Two things to note. Firstly, the question specified diameter, but we must use the radius – an old trap! Secondly, we keep π in the answer so as to keep the values exact.

So, volume of cone:volume of hemisphere = 270π:486π = 5π:9π = **5:9**

The diagram shows a cone on top of a cylinder. Find the surface area and the volume.

The circle at the base of the cone will not form part of the surface area since it is inside the shape. You will need Pythagoras' Theorem to calculate the slant height of the cone.

$A = 353\text{cm}^2$, $V = 493\text{cm}^3$

11.4cm

6cm

8cm

A cylindrical tube of length 40cm and radius 3.2cm contains 6 tennis balls each with a radius of 3.14cm.

Giving answers to 3SF:
a)   Find the volume of the tube.
b)   Find the volume of one tennis ball.
c)   Hence find the volume of empty space in the tube.
       You will need the total volume of the 6 tennis balls.

(a) **1287cm³**   (b) **130cm³**   (c) **509cm³**

The question above is a good example of the importance of *working* to more than 3SF. If you used the first two rounded answers to calculate the third, you would have arrived at 507cm³.

      1287 − 6 × 130 = 507
      1286.79 − 6 × 129.68 = 508.71

Further geometry practice:
1.   a)   An observer on a ship which is 2.3km from the coast measures the angle of elevation of a cliff as 2°. Find the height of the cliff in metres.
        b)   A 35m tower stands on the edge of the cliff. Find the angle of depression for an observer looking at the ship from the top of the tower.

2.   Three boats P, Q and R are at anchor in a bay. The bearing of P from R is 046°, and of Q from P is 125°. The distance of R from P is 3km, and of P from Q is 4km.
        a)   Draw a clear diagram showing all the information.
        b)   Calculate:
            i)   the distance of R from Q;
            ii)   the bearing of R from Q.

3.   The diagram shows a right pyramid with:
        PQ = 8cm, QR = 6cm, VW = 12cm.
        W is at the centre of the base, M and N are the midpoints of PQ and QR. Calculate:
        a)   PR
        b)   PV
        c)   Angle VPW
        d)   VM
        e)   The angle VM makes with the base
        f)   MN
        g)   Angle MSN *(Draw triangle MSN first)*

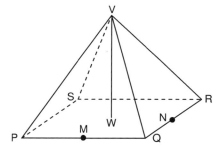

4.   A solid cone of height 6cm and radius 2cm is melted down to be made into small spheres. If each sphere has a radius of 0.5cm, how many can be made?

ANSWERS

1.   80.3m, 2.87°
2.   5.44km, 272.2°
3.   10cm, 13cm, 67.4°, 12.4cm, 76.0°, 5cm, 40.6°
4.   Volume of cone = 25.1cm³,
        Volume of each sphere = 0.524cm³
        Makes 47 spheres, with a bit left over!

MATHEMATICAL MODELS
Basics of Functions

A function is an algebraic rule which shows how one set of numbers is related to, or obtained from another set. Functions often model real-life situations, so you must understand the different types of function and the notation and terminology used.

Read the definition as: "The function f takes any number x and turns it into $x^2 - 1$"

Defining functions: A function is defined using the notation $f(x) = ...$, for example: $f(x) = x^2 - 1$. This notation can show what happens when a specific value of x is input to the function: for example, $f(3) = 3^2 - 1 = 8$. The x value put in to the function is called the *object* and the value of the function which results is called the *image*. Letters other than f and x are often used.

Domain: The set of values to be put into a function is called the *domain* of the function. In many functions, *any* value can be input, in which case the domain is $x \in \square$. However, the domain may be restricted in a particular question. For example, suppose the x numbers in a function are limited to integers greater than 0; we can show the domain like this:

$$f(x) = 2x + 3, x > 0, x \in \square$$

In exam questions the domain will be the set of all real numbers unless otherwise stated.

Range: The set of values produced by a function is called the *range*. For example, the function defined by $f(x) = x^2$ has a range $f(x) \geq 0$ since it is impossible for squares to be negative. Generally, the easiest way to find the range of a function is to look at its graph: the range is the complete set of possible y values.

Mathematical models: The emphasis throughout this section of the syllabus is on functions as *models* of real-life situations. If a car is travelling at a constant speed, then the distance travelled against the time taken can be modelled as a linear function such as $d = 80t$. Population growth, however, is not linear – if a country's population has grown by 100,000 in one year, it will probably grow by more than that the next year and so on. Population growth is usually modelled using an *exponential* function. The function may not model the real-life situation exactly, but mathematicians can try and develop more complex functions to increase the accuracy of a model.

Graphs: Every function can be graphed: we have already looked at the graphs of linear (straight line) functions. Each type of function has a graph with a distinctive shape, and with particular properties. The graphs are important: they give us a *picture* of how each function behaves – when is it increasing or decreasing, when does it have zero value, what happens as the x values become increasingly large. The GDC is of course very useful for graph drawing, but you should also be able to recognise the type of function from a sketch graph.

What is the difference between drawing and sketching? (Find out later)!

We first look at the different types of functions you are expected to know, and then we look at the various techniques for sketching and drawing graphs.

Linear Functions

Burgers cost £1.50 each. The table on the right shows how, as the number of burgers (x) increases steadily, so does the cost (y); the function connecting the two is *linear* because when the values are plotted on a graph the points form a straight *line*.

Burgers	Cost
1	1.50
2	3.00
3	4.50
4	6.00
5	7.50

Equations of straight lines: The equations of straight lines were discussed on page 46. Also note the following:

- Lines of the form $x = k$ are vertical
- Lines of the form $y = k$ are horizontal
- Lines of the form $y = kx$ go through (0, 0) and have gradient k (remember that a gradient of 2, for example, means that when the line goes along 1 it goes up 2)
- Lines of the form $x + y = a$ go through (0, a) and (a, 0).

Important lines to remember:

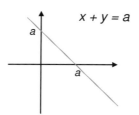

John wants some posters printed to advertise a concert. The printer tells him that it will cost $510 to print 100 posters and $630 to print 300 posters.

a)   Plot the two points on a graph where 1cm represents 50 posters on the x axis, and 1cm represents $100 on the y axis, and join them to form a line.
b)   Where does the line cross the y axis?
c)   What is the gradient of the line?
d)   Write down the formula connecting the cost (y) to the number of posters printed (x).
e)   John can spend up to $780. How many posters could he get printed?

b)   The line crosses the y axis at **$450**. (This represents the basic cost to the printer of setting up the printing process).

c)   The gradient of the line is $\dfrac{630-510}{300-100} = $ **0.6**. (This represents the cost of printing each individual poster).

d) $y = 450 + 0.6x$ (Note that we don't include units in the equations of lines).

e) $780 = 450 + 0.6x$
        $270 = 0.6x$
        $450 = x$ So John could have **550** posters printed.

Quadratic Functions

The graph of a quadratic function has been mentioned on page 12 with regard to the solution of quadratic equations. The following notes relate to the general quadratic function $y = ax^2 + bx + c$

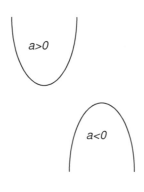

Properties of quadratic graphs: All quadratic graphs are parabolas, the sign of a determining "which way up." The value of c is the y-intercept. For example, the graph of $y = x^2 + 3x - 4$ cuts the y-axis at (0, -4) and is in the shape of a U. We can find the x-intercepts by solving the equation $x^2 + 3x - 4 = 0$ (either by GDC or by factorisation), giving $x = -4$ or $x = 1$.

- Thus the x-intercepts are at (-4, 0) and (1, 0).

The graph is always symmetrical about the vertical line passing through the vertex (turning point), a fact which can often be used when answering questions about the graph. The line of symmetry is always $x = \dfrac{-b}{2a}$.

- $y = x^2 + 3x - 4$ has a line of symmetry at $x = -3/2 = -1.5$

Also note that the line of symmetry is midway between the x-intercepts.

The vertex is also on the line of symmetry, so its y-coordinate can be calculated by substituting into the equation:

- When $x = -1.5$, $y = (-1.5)^2 + 3 \times (-1.5) - 4 = -6.25$, so the vertex is at (-1.5, -6.25)

Summarising:

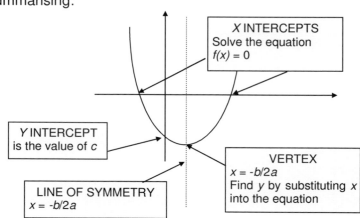

```
X INTERCEPTS
Solve the equation
f(x) = 0
```

```
Y INTERCEPT
is the value of c
```

```
LINE OF SYMMETRY
x = -b/2a
```

```
VERTEX
x = -b/2a
Find y by substituting x
into the equation
```

If you know the x-intercepts, then these can be used to work back to the equation. In general, if the x-intercepts are p and q, then the quadratic equation will be of the form $y = a(x - p)(x - q)$; a can be found using other information in the question.

The graph has equation $y = a(x - p)(x - q)$. The x-intercepts are at (1, 0) and (5, 0), and the vertex is at $(h, 12)$.

a) **Write down the values of p and q.**
   $p = 1$, $q = 5$.
b) **Find the value of h.**
   h is midway between the x-intercepts. $h = 3$
c) **Find the value a.**
   Substituting the point (3, 12):
   $12 = a(3 - 1)(3 - 5) \Rightarrow 12 = -4a \Rightarrow a = -3$
d) **Write down the y-intercept.**
   The y-intercept is at (0, -15)

Factorisation: Although not specifically in the Studies syllabus, quadratic factorisation is a useful technique which can speed up the solution of many quadratic equations. Factorising is the opposite of multiplying out. Quadratic factorisation can come in three forms:

- $ax^2 + bx$ - use common factors
  eg: $2x^2 - 6x = 2x(x - 3)$
- $a^2x^2 - b^2$ - the "difference of two squares"
  eg: $x^2 - 36 = x^2 - 6^2 = (x - 6)(x + 6)$
  $4x^2 - 49 = (2x)^2 - 7^2 = (2x - 7)(2x + 7)$
  and you may have to use common factors first:
  eg: $2x^2 - 50 = 2(x^2 - 25) = 2(x - 5)(x + 5)$
  You just have to be able to recognise the types of expression which factorise like this. Note particularly that expressions of the form $x^2 + a^2$ do *not* factorise.
- $x^2 + bx + c$ - factorise into two brackets. You must first find two numbers which add to give b and multiply to give c (taking signs into account)
  eg: $x^2 + 8x + 15$. The two numbers are 3 and 5, so:
  $x^2 + 8x + 15 = (x + 3)(x + 5)$
  eg: $x^2 - 3x - 10$. The two numbers are -5 and +2, so:
  $x^2 - 3x - 10 = (x - 5)(x + 2)$
  eg: $x^2 - 10x + 24$. The two numbers are -6 and -4, so:
  $x^2 - 10x + 24 = (x - 6)(x - 4)$

Difference of two squares

The factorisation derives from the fact that
$(a - b)(a + b) = a^2 - b^2$

The factorised form also tells us where the x-intercepts are on the related quadratic graph. For $y = (x - a)(x - b)$, the x-intercepts are at $x = a$ and at $x = b$. So, for the graph of $y = x^2 + 8x + 15$ (see above), the x-intercepts will be at (-3, 0) and (-5, 0).

Solving quadratic equations: To solve a quadratic equation using factorisation, you must make sure that the equation has 0 on the right hand side. If necessary, you must rearrange the equation first. In factorised form, equations solve like this:

- $(x - 6)(x - 4) = 0 \Rightarrow x = 4$ or 6
- $(x - 5)(x + 2) = 0 \Rightarrow x = 5$ or -2
- $2x(x - 3) = 0 \Rightarrow x = 0$ or 3
- $(x + 6)(x - 6) = 0 \Rightarrow x = -6$ or 6

This is because if $p \times q = 0$ it follows that either $p = 0$ or $q = 0$. So in the first example, either $x - 6 = 0$ or $x - 4 = 0$, giving $x = 6$ or 4.

Try solving the following quadratic equations using factorisation:

1. $x^2 - 11x + 28 = 0$
2. $x^2 + 5x = 0$
3. $x^2 + 9x - 10 = 0$
4. $x^2 + 5x + 6 = 0$
5. $x^2 + 5x - 6 = 0$
6. $2x^2 - 200 = 0$
7. $x^2 + 10x - 36 = 2x + 12$

ANSWERS
1. $x = 4$ or 7
2. $x = 0$ or -5
3. $x = -10$ or 1
4. $x = -2$ or -3
5. $x = -6$ or 1
6. $x = = 10$ or -10
7. $x = -12$ or 4

Exponential Functions

Exponential functions are based on the function $f(x) = a^x$. Typical real life situations which can be modelled by exponential functions are population growth (eg: population increases by 1% per year) compound interest (eg: investment increases by 6% per year) and radioactive decay (eg: mass decreases by 10% every 30 years). One important feature of any exponential function is that the time taken to multiply by a certain amount (say, double) is always the same.

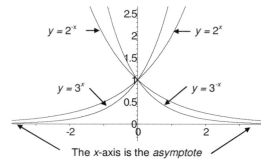

The x-axis is the *asymptote*

Graphs: Exponential graphs are *asymptotic* – that is, they get closer and closer to a line without ever reaching it. Exponential graphs which increase are based on $y = a^x$; those which decrease are based on $y = a^{-x}$. Also, $y = a^x$ always passes through (0, 1) for any value of a (because $a^0 = 1$).

Graphs of other exponential functions: The graph of $y = ka^x$ is the same as $y = a^x$ but stretched by k in the y direction. Key features are:
- x-axis is the asymptote
- y-intercept is (0, k)
- graph is steeper than $y = a^x$

The graph of $y = a^x + c$ is the same as $y = a^x$ but moved upwards by a distance c. Key features are:
- $x = c$ is the asymptote
- y-intercept is (0, c)
- graph is parallel to $y = a^x$

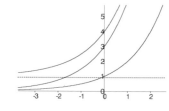

The graphs on the left are: $y = 2^x$, $y = 3 \times 2^x$, $y = 3 \times 2^x + 1$; work out which is which.

Complete the table of values for the exponential function $y = 4^x$. For this function, find the value of x when $f(x) = 65536$.

x	0	1	2	3	4
f(x)			16	64	

To answer the second part, use your calculator to find what power of 4 gives 65536.

1, 4, 256 $x = 8$

An experiment is devised to measure the rate of bacteria growth. The number of bacteria, B, at a time t minutes after the start of the experiment is given by the formula:

$$B = p \times 2^t + q$$

The number of bacteria when $t = 0$ is 34.
The number of bacteria when $t = 3$ is 62.

a) Write down two equations using this information and hence find the values of p and q.
b) Calculate the number of bacteria when $t = 4.5$
c) After how many minutes will there be 392 bacteria?

You will need to solve an equation using your GDC.

(a) $34 = p + q$, $62 = p \times 8 + q$; $p = 4$, $q = 30$ (b) 120   (c) 6.5 minutes

More General Functions

The functions we have seen so far each belong to a particular "family", and the graphs for each type of function are similar. More generally, you are expected to be able to deal with functions of the form $f(x) = ax^m + bx^n + \ldots$ where m, n and so on are integers. If the powers are all positive, then the graph of the function will be similar to a quadratic graph, but probably with more turning points (see right).

However, remember that $x^{-1} = \dfrac{1}{x}$; if x appears on the bottom line

within a function then this will always create a *vertical asymptote* on the graph of the function. This is because division by 0 isn't possible, and trying to divide by 0 creates a "barrier" on the graph as x increases from left to right. The graph on the left shows the function $f(x) = x^2 - \dfrac{3}{x}$, and we can see that the y axis is in fact a vertical asymptote to the graph. Apart from $x = 0$, all other x values can be input to the function.

Using the GDC: In the exam you will be expected to be able to do the following on your GDC:

- Enter the function
- Draw the graph of the function in an appropriate window
- Identify key points on the graph (eg: intercepts)
- Copy the graph onto paper
- Solve equations using the function.

Entering the function into your GDC: Make sure you know your GDC keys well enough to be able to enter functions with confidence, in particular entering powers and exponential functions. Most modern calculators have displays which show correct mathematical notation: however, you must be careful entering a function such as 2^{x+3} to ensure you don't accidentally enter $2^x + 3$. In many cases, using brackets provides you with a safety net.

Selecting the appropriate window: Although your GDC has some standard graph scales, you will often have to set up the window manually by typing in minimum and maximum values for the axes. If you are not sure what window to set, creating a table for the function gives you an idea of the range of y values (you will always be given the domain, that is, the set of x values to use).

For example, take the function $y = x^3 + 5x^2 + x$, $-5 \leq x \leq 1$. The first screenshot below shows the graph with the standard scales (-10 to 10). Now let's create a table of values, and we see that the range for y is -5 to 15. Change the window, and see the improvement!

In fact, I set the y axis to show values from -6 to 16.

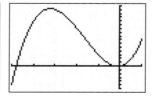

Identifying key points: Having drawn the graph on your GDC, you should be able to do the following:

- Enter an x value and find the value of y, the function value. (For example, the question may ask you to find $f(1.5)$.)
- Find the x-intercept(s) – this may be called the "zero" on your calculator. Remember that you can only find one intercept at a time, so you need to know how to find all of them.
- Find any minimum and maximum points (see also the next chapter on differentiation).
- Find the point of intersection of two graphs.

Creating a sketch of the graph on paper: "Drawing" a graph usually means plotting a number of individual points and joining them up. A "sketch" shows the axes and the graph with any key points labelled. The axes do not have to have scales, but any intercepts should be shown. Asymptotes can be shown as dotted lines, and labelled with their equations.

For example, I've sketched two graphs and you can see my sketches below, alongside the graphs on the GDC. The two equations are: $y = x^3 - 3x + 1$ and $y = 2^x + \dfrac{1}{x+1}$. In both cases, I used $-2 \le x \le 2$.

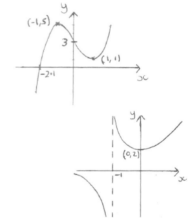

Solving equations: Your GDC will have a built-in equation solver, but often the easiest way to solve an equation is:

- Rearrange to make the right hand side zero
- Draw the graph
- Find where the graph cuts the x-axis

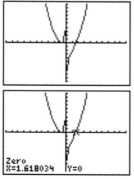

For example, solve $x^2 - 2 = \dfrac{1}{x}$, $x > 0$. Rearrange to form the equation $x^2 - 2 - \dfrac{1}{x} = 0$, and then draw the graph (see left). Now use the "zero" function on the GDC, and we can see that the solution of the equation is $x = 1.62$.

The solution could also be found by drawing the graphs of $y = x^2 - 2$ and $y = \dfrac{1}{x}$ and then finding the x-coordinate of their point of intersection.

$f(x) = x^3 \times 2^{-x}$, $x \geq 0$.

a) **Sketch the graph of $f(x)$, showing its asymptotic behaviour.**
The domain is x ≥ 0. The asymptote is the x-axis, so I have drawn the graph far enough over to indicate that. There is no vertical asymptote. I've put the scales in, but just a couple of numbers to give an idea of scale would be good enough.

b) **Find the co-ordinates of the maximum point, and hence state the range of $f(x)$.**
Maximum at **(4.33, 4.04)** GDC. So the range is $0 \leq y \leq 4.04$.

c) **Draw a line on your graph to show that $f(x) = 1$ has two solutions.**
I've drawn the line y = 1 and this intersects the graph of f(x) twice.

d) **Find the solutions to $f(x) = 1$, giving your answers to 3 significant figures.**
Since I already had the two lines on the graph, I used the GDC to find the two points of intersection. It's the x values which are the solutions. So: $x = 1.37$ and $x = 9.94$

---

a) **Sketch the graph of the function $f(x) = \dfrac{2x+4}{x+3}$, $-10 \leq x \leq 10$. Indicate clearly the axis intercepts and any asymptotes.**

b) **Write down the equation of the vertical asymptote.**

c) **On the same diagram sketch the graph of $g(x) = 4 - x$**

d) **Find the solution to the equation $\dfrac{2x+4}{x+3} = 4 - x$ where $x > 0$. Give your answer to four decimal places.**

b) Vertical asymptote is $x = -3$
d) $x = 2.3723$

Two functions are given by $f(x) = \dfrac{2}{x^2+1}$ and $g(x) = \sqrt{x+1}$.

a) **Sketch the graphs of $f(x)$ and $g(x)$ on the same diagram, with values of x between -3 and 3, and values of y between -1 and 3. Label each curve and any axis intercepts.**

b) **How many solutions exist for the equation $\dfrac{2}{x^2+1} - \sqrt{x+1} = 0$?**

c) **Find a solution for the equation in part (b). Give your answer to 4 significant figures.**

b) 1
c) $x = 0.7235$

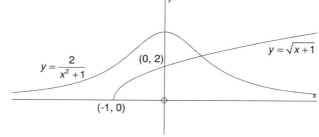

INTRODUCTION TO DIFFERENTIAL CALCULUS

Gradients of Curves

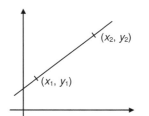

Gradient of a straight line: The gradient of the line joining two points (x_1, y_1) and (x_2, y_2) is calculated using the formula $\dfrac{y_2 - y_1}{x_2 - x_1}$.

This gives a single number which represents the rate of change of y compared to x. If the graph represents "real-life" quantities, then the gradient will have a meaning as well. Examples are:

x	y	Gradient
Time	Distance	Rate of change of distance = velocity
Time	Amount of water in a bath	Rate of increase of volume
No. of promotional brochures (in hundreds)	Cost of printing the brochures (in £)	Cost per hundred brochures

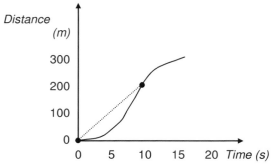

Average gradient: When a curved graph is drawn, it does not have a single value to represent gradient. But by drawing a straight line between any two points, the *average* gradient between the points can be calculated. Consider a car accelerating from rest:

At time 0s, it is at its start position. At time 10s, it is 200m away. The gradient of the line joining these points is 20, so its average speed for the first 10 seconds is 20m/s.

Note three things:
- At the start it will be going less than 20m/s, at the end it will be going more.
- This information could have been worked out from a table – the graph is not *necessary* to work out average gradients.
- We could work out an average gradient between *any* two points.

Gradient at a point on a curve: In the example above we calculated the average speed of the car between two times, but we know that the speedo on the car will register the actual speed at a single moment. This is equivalent to the gradient of the curve at a single point. The gradient can be calculated by drawing a *tangent* to the curve and calculating the gradient of the tangent.

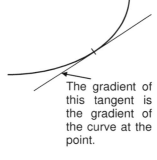

The gradient of this tangent is the gradient of the curve at the point.

Special points: You should know the following special points on curves:

A *minimum*. The gradient is zero. To the left the gradient is <0, to the right it is >0.

A *maximum*. The gradient is zero. To the left the gradient is >0, to the right it is <0.

At each of these points the zero gradient means that the function is momentarily neither increasing or decreasing.

Between the special points: Don't forget that the gradient represents the rate of change of *y* (ie the function) compared to *x*.

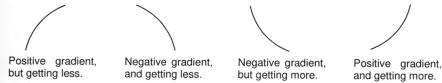

Positive gradient, but getting less.

Negative gradient, and getting less.

Negative gradient, but getting more.

Positive gradient, and getting more.

Calculating the gradient at a point:
Suppose we want to find the gradient of $y = x^2$ at the point (3,9).

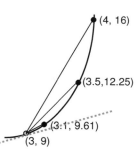

The diagram on the right shows part of the curve and the grey, dotted line is the *tangent* at (3,9). The gradient of this line will be the gradient of the curve at the point. Imagine the black dot sliding down the curve: we can calculate the average gradient from (3, 9) to the dot as it passes various points.

(3,9) → (4,16)   Ave. Grad. = 7
(3,9) → (3.5,12.25)   Ave. Grad. = 6.5
(3,9) → (3.1,9.61)   Ave. Grad. = 6.1

And as we slide down, the average gradients get closer and closer to the gradient at the point. We can guess that it will be about 6, but we can use a formula to confirm this value.

The formula for gradient at a point: By generalising the process of the last section, we can find the gradient at a point (*x*, *y*) on the curve of $y = f(x)$ by using the formula:

$$\text{Gradient} = \lim_{h \to 0} \left(\frac{f(x+h) - f(x)}{h} \right)$$

- *h* is a small distance in the *x* direction
- "lim" stands for limit: we want to know what the value of the formula is as *h* gets ever closer to 0

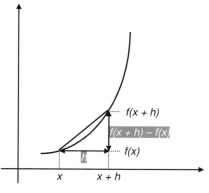

In our example above, $f(x) = x^2$ and $x = 3$.
So the gradient at $x = 3$ can be calculated as:

$$\lim_{h \to 0} \left(\frac{(3+h)^2 - 3^2}{h} \right) = \lim_{h \to 0} \left(\frac{9 + 6h + h^2 - 3^2}{h} \right) = \lim_{h \to 0} \left(\frac{6h + h^2}{h} \right) = \lim_{h \to 0} (6 + h)$$

As *h* gets close to 0, the limit of this formula is 6: this is the gradient at $x = 3$.

Although you will not be expected to use the formal idea of limits in the exam, you should understand the general principle that the average gradient between two points on a curve gets closer and closer to the gradient at the lower point as the upper one slides towards it (or, of course, the other way around). For example, you may be asked to explain what the formula gives you in a certain situation, and the answer will be "the gradient at the point."

Differentiation

If we had to go through the above calculation every time we wanted a gradient it would be very time consuming. Fortunately, the gradients of functions form distinct rules; applying a rule to find the gradient is called *differentiation*.

Differentiation of polynomials: The only functions you need to be able to differentiate are those with terms of the form ax^n, where n can be any integer (including negative).

In general, differentiating ax^n gives nax^{n-1}; in other words, "multiply in front by the power and reduce the power by 1." Note in particular that a term such as $6x$ becomes 6 when differentiated, and a constant (such as 3) becomes 0.

The function you get when you differentiate is called the *derived function* or the *derivative*; think of it as the *gradient function* because it enables you to work out the gradient at any point. The

The function may be expressed using letters other than x and y. For example, if $h = 2t - 10t^2$ then the notation would be either $h'(t)$ or $\dfrac{dh}{dt}$.

notation used for the derived function is $\dfrac{dy}{dx}$ or $f'(x)$, not to be confused with $f^{-1}(x)$ for the inverse function. Some examples of derived functions are:

$f(x)$	$f'(x)$
$3x^2 - 4x + 1$	$6x - 4$
$\frac{1}{3}x^3 - 2x$	$x^2 - 2$
$(x-1)(x-3) = x^2 - 4x + 3$	$2x - 4$
$\dfrac{2}{x^2} = 2x^{-2}$	$-4x^{-3} = \dfrac{-4}{x^3}$

Calculating the gradient at a point: The procedure is:
- Differentiate the function
- Substitute the x-coordinate into the derived function to get the gradient (note that the y-coordinate is irrelevant).

You may also be *given* the gradient at a point and asked to find which point it is. In this case, the procedure is:
- Differentiate the function
- Put the derived function equal to the given gradient
- Solve the equation to find x
- Find the y-coordinate from the original function (if asked).

For the curve $y = 4x - 2x^3$

i)   **Find the gradient at the point (-1, -2)**

If $y = 4x - 2x^3$ then $\dfrac{dy}{dx} = 4 - 6x^2$. When $x = -1$, $\dfrac{dy}{dx} = 4 - 6 = $ **-2**

ii)   **Find the points where the gradient = 2.5**

We need to solve the equation $4 - 6x^2 = 2.5$

$$4 - 6x^2 = 2.5$$
$$1.5 = 6x^2$$
$$x^2 = 0.25$$
$$x = \pm 0.5$$

When $x = 0.5$, $y = 4 \times 0.5 - 2 \times (0.5)^3 = 1.75$
When $x = -0.5$, $y = 4 \times (-0.5) - 2 \times (-0.5)^3 = -1.75$

So the gradient is 2.5 at **(0.5, 1.75)** and **(-0.5, -1.75)**

Tangents and Normals

Tangent to a curve: Since differentiation gives us a way to calculate the gradient of a curve at any point, we can extend the calculation to work out the equation of the tangent to a curve at any point. On page 46 you will find the method for finding the equation of a straight line given a point and the gradient, although in the next question I demonstrate the use of an alternative formula. We now have all the tools we need.

The diagram shows a sketch of the graph of $y = x^2 - 4x + 3$.

a) Write down the co-ordinates of the point P where the graph crosses the y axis.

b) Show that the equation of the tangent to the point P is $y + 4x = 3$.

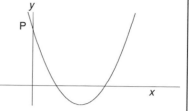

a) When $x = 0$, $y = 0 - 0 + 3$. So the co-ordinates of P are (0,3)

b) First we must differentiate the function to find the gradient.

$$y = x^2 - 4x + 3$$

$$\frac{dy}{dx} = 2x - 4$$

So when $x = 0$, $\frac{dy}{dx} = -4$ (Check: the graph is going down at P, so -4 seems OK)

Equation of a straight line is $y - y_1 = m(x - x_1)$
So the equation of the tangent at P is $y - 3 = -4(x - 0)$
$$y - 3 = -4x$$
$$4x + y = 3$$

A curve has equation $y = x^2 - \dfrac{3}{x}$.

a) Find $\dfrac{dy}{dx}$ for this curve.

b) Find the gradient of the curve at the point P where $x = -1$.

c) Show that the tangent to the curve at P has equation $y = x + 5$.

Be very careful with minus signs.

(a) $2x + 3/x^2$,   (b) 1

Equations of normals: A tangent to a curve at a point has the same gradient as the curve at that point; a *normal* is perpendicular to the curve at that point. The procedure for finding the equation of the normal is exactly the same as for the tangent, except that we need to use the formula on page 45 for finding the gradient of one line which is perpendicular to another.

So, in the first question above, the gradient of the normal at P is $\frac{1}{4}$; check that this gives the equation of the normal as $4y - x = 12$. And in the second question, check that the normal at the point where $x = -1$ is $x + y = 3$.

Using the GDC: Find out how to draw the tangent to a curve on your GDC; when you draw the tangent, you should find that the equation will be displayed as well – see the screenshot on the right which displays the answer to the second question above. Note that if you enter the equation of the normal, it will only *look* perpendicular to the tangent if you are using the equal scales view.

A function is defined by $f(x) = \dfrac{2}{x^2} + 2x + k,\ x \neq 0,\ k \in \mathbb{Q}$

a) The graph of $f(x)$ passes through the point P = (1, 1). Find the value of k.

Substitute (1, 1) into the function to get: $1 = \dfrac{2}{1} + 2 + k$ So k = -3.

b) Differentiate $f(x)$.

$$f(x) = \frac{2}{x^2} + 2x - 3 = 2x^{-2} + 2x - 3$$

$$f'(x) = -4x^{-3} + 2 = -\frac{4}{x^3} + 2$$

Let L be the tangent to the graph of f at point P.

c) **(i)** Show that the gradient of L is -2.
   (ii) Find the equation of L.

The x-coordinate of P is 1. Substitute into the "gradient function" $f'(x)$:

When x = 1, $f'(x) = \dfrac{-4}{1} + 2 = -4 + 2$ = -2

So the equation of L is y = -2x + c. Now substitute (1, 1) to find the value of c.
$\qquad\qquad$ 1 = -2 +c and so c = 3
$\qquad\qquad\qquad$ The equation of L is **y = -2x + 3**

d) **L intersects the graph again at Q. Find the coordinates of Q.**
$\qquad$ Q = (-0.5, 4) (GDC)

Further differentiation practice:
1. Differentiate:

$\qquad$ (a) $3x^2 - 4x + 5$; (b) $3 - 8x^3$; (c) $4x + 3 - \dfrac{2}{x} + \dfrac{1}{x^2}$

2. For each of the curves in the previous question, find the gradient at the point where x = 2, and where x = -2.

3. Find the two points on the graph of $y = x^3 - 3x^2 + 5$ where the gradient of the graph is 9.

4. For the function $f(x) = 2x - \dfrac{4}{x} + 1$

$\qquad$ a) The point P = (2, a) lies on the graph of f. Find the value of a.
$\qquad$ b) Find the equation of the tangent to the graph at P.
$\qquad$ c) Find the equation of the normal to the graph at P.
$\qquad$ d) Sketch the graph for values of x between -4 and 3. On the same graph, sketch the tangent and normal lines found in parts (b) and (c).
$\qquad$ e) Where does the normal cut the curve again?

ANSWERS

1. (a) $6x - 4$; (b) $-24x^2$; (c) $4 + \dfrac{2}{x^2} - \dfrac{2}{x^3}$ (or $4 + 2x^{-2} - 2x^{-3}$)

2. 8, -96, 4.25; -16, -96, 4.75
3. (-1, 1), (3, 5)
4. (a) a = 3 (b) $y = 3x - 3$
$\qquad$ (c) $x + 3y = 11$
$\qquad$ (e) (-1.02, 2,86)

Maximum and Minimum Points

Finding the turning points on a graph is particularly useful because such points tell us about the maximum and minimum values of the function. We can find these points by putting the gradient function equal to zero – but which point is which? We can find out by looking at the gradient either side of the turning point. (The procedure is:

- Differentiate the function
- Form an equation by equating the derived function to 0
- Solve the equation to find the x value of the turning point
- Find the y value if required
- Find the gradient either side of the turning point by drawing a *sign diagram*
- From the sign diagram, decide if you have a maximum or a minimum.

A retailer, for example, may be able to construct a function which relates the profit he makes to the selling price of his product. Too low a price, he doesn't cover his costs; too high a price, it doesn't sell. Somewhere in between he can find the selling price which gives the maximum profit – this will be the turning point on his graph.

The height h m of a kite t secs after being launched is given by $h = t^3 - 4t^2 + 4t, 0 \le t \le 3$

a) Find the height of the kite after 0.5s and after 1s.

Substitute t = 0.5 into the velocity to get $h = 1.125\text{ms}^{-1}$
Substitute t = 1 into the velocity to get $h = 1\text{ms}^{-1}$

b) Find $\dfrac{dh}{dt}$ in terms of t. Find the values of t at the local maximum and local minimum values of the function.

$\dfrac{dh}{dt} = 3t^2 - 8t + 4$. For a max or min, $\dfrac{dh}{dt} = 0$, so:

$$3t^2 - 8t + 4 = 0$$
$$(3t - 2)(t - 2) = 0 \quad (\text{or use GDC})$$

So the turning points are at $t = 0.667$ and $t = 2$.

The question did not ask us to identify which is the maximum and which the minimum, but the sign diagram is drawn up like this:

- Choose values of t either side of the turning point(s)
- Draw up a table showing these values and the turning point values
- Work out the gradient at each point (you only need to know if it is >0, =0 or <0) by substituting into the derived function
- Identify the nature of the points

t	0	0.667	1	2	3
Gradient	>0 (4)	0	<0 (-1)	0	>0 (7)
	/	—	\	—	/

So at $t = 0.667$ there is a maximum and at $t = 2$ there is a minimum. What do these turning points represent? They show when the height is *locally* at its greatest or at its least. The graph of the function is:

The minimum and maximum are called local because they only represent least and greatest values of the function in that part of the graph.

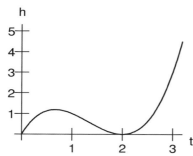

So the kite starts rising at $t = 0$ until $t = 0.667$. At this point it starts going down until it hits the ground momentarily at $t = 2$, then it rises again. The formula is only valid until $t = 3$, so we don't know what happens after then. Looking at the graph purely as a function, note the following:

- Between $t = 0$ and $t = 0.667$, the function is *increasing*.
- At $t = 0.667$ the function is *stationary* (neither increasing nor decreasing). This is known as a *stationary point*.
- Between $t = 0.667$ and $t = 2$ the function is *decreasing*.
- At $t = 2$ the function is again stationary.
- For all values of t greater than 2 the function is *increasing*.

Consider the function $f(x) = x^2 - 4x^{-1}$, $-4 \le x \le 4$, $x \ne 0$.

a)   Write down the equation of the vertical asymptote.

b)   Find $f'(x)$.

c)   Write down the coordinates of the stationary point, and state whether it is a maximum or a minimum.

d)   Write down all the intervals for which $f(x)$ is increasing within the given domain.

(a) $x = 0$ (b) $f'(x) = 2x + 4x^{-2}$ (c) (-1.26, 4.76), Minimum (GDC)

(d) -1.26 $\le x < 0$, $0 < x \le 4$.

Note carefully the intervals in part (d). x cannot be 0, so I have used < rather than $\le$; and because of the vertical asymptote I have split the answer into two separate intervals. The top of the second interval is 4 because that is the highest value of x in this question.

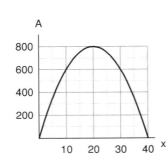

Optimization problems: Look back to the question at the top of page 13. We were enclosing a garden with 3 sections of fence with a total length of 80m, and we found the enclosed area could be expressed as $A = 80x - 2x^2$. In that question we then went on to find x if the enclosed area were 600m^2. Suppose instead we wanted to find the *maximum* area achievable with 80m of fencing – this is an optimization problem. In other words, find the dimensions of the rectangle which give the optimum area (maximum in this case).

The graph on the left shows how the area varies as x increases to its highest possible value of 40m. It would appear that the maximum area occurs when $x = 20$m. We can prove this by differentiation since the maximum value occurs when $\dfrac{dA}{dx} = 0$. So:

$$\frac{dA}{dx} = 80 - 4x$$

$$0 = 80 - 4x$$

$$4x = 80 \Rightarrow x = 20$$

So the dimensions of the garden will be 20m × 40m, giving the maximum area of 800m^2.

A ship is to make a voyage of 200km travelling at a constant speed. When this speed is v km/h, the cost is $\$(v^2 + 16000/v)$ per hour. Find the speed at which the ship should travel to minimise this cost. Find also the time taken for the voyage, and the cost.

Differentiating the expression for the cost we get $2v - 16000/v^2$, and this must equal 0 for a minimum. This gives $v = 20$km/h. At 20km/h the voyage of 200km takes 10 hours. The cost is $1200 per hour, giving a total cost of $12000.

PRACTICE QUESTIONS

The questions which follow are not designed to cover every aspect of the syllabus, nor are they exam style questions. Their purpose is to give you some practice in the *basics*: if you cannot, for example, carry out a straightforward differentiation, then you will get questions which depend on accurate differentiation wrong, even if you know exactly how to do the question. So you need to answer all these questions as part of your revision. If you get an answer wrong, find out why: then come back to it later, and see if you can get it right next time.

NUMBER AND ALGEBRA

1. Calculate $\dfrac{4.523}{6.81 \times 2.47}$ giving your answer to 3 SF.

2. A triangle has a base of 12.5 cm and a height of 7.8 cm, both measurements to 1 D.P. What is the maximum possible area?

3. What is the percentage error if the fraction $\frac{22}{7}$ is used for π?

4. If a computer carries out 5.6×10^9 calculations per second, how long does 1 calculation take. Give your answer in standard form.

5. Convert 58 km/h into m/s.

6. Find the 25th term and the sum of the first 54 terms of the sequence which begins: 3, 8, 13, 18 …

7. An arithmetic sequence has first term 7 and common difference 3.5. How many terms are required for the sum of the sequence to be 25830.

8. What is the 12th term and the sum to 18 terms of the sequence which begins 3, 12, 48, 192?

9. A geometric series has a first term 400, ten terms and a sum of 1295.67. What is the common ratio?

10. How much will an investment of $6300 be worth (to the nearest dollar) after accumulating compound interest for 12 years at a rate of 3% per annum? If 1.5% interest is paid every 6 months, how much will the investment be worth after 12 years?

11. Find the solution of the simultaneous equations $2y = 3x + 5$ and $6x + 3y = 11$.

12. Rearrange the equation $3x^2 + 5x = x^2 - 2$ so that the right hand side equals 0. Solve the equation using a calculator method.

13. If £3.50 = €5.39, convert £1 to €, and €1 to £.

14. If $1 = 12.8 crowns, how many dollars would 150 crowns be worth?

15. A bank charges commission when converting currency as follows: the charge is 5% or $3.50, whichever is larger. Using the conversion rate in question 14, how many crowns would a customer receive when changing $50? And how many crowns for $500.

16. I invest $2500 at 3% compound interest. How much will my investment be worth in 10 years? What would be the equivalent rate of simple interest?

17. How many years will it take for an investment of £1500 to grow to £2500 at a rate of 6%, compounded annually?

18. I buy a car for €9000 and it depreciates at 30% per year for two years and then at 20% per year for another 3 years. How much will it then be worth, to the nearest euro?

19. How much more would a £5200 investment be worth after 4 years if the compound interest rate is 0.5% per month instead of 6% per year?

20. Set up a table on your GDC which shows the annual value of a $200 investment growing at 4% compound interest per year. Use your table to write down after how many years the investment will be worth more than $300 and after how many years it will have trebled in value.

DESCRIPTIVE STATISTICS

15.60	5.95	31.22	3.02	6.60	24.70	15.45	32.50	12.45	4.43
12.65	10.09	52.86	12.88	2.53	31.79	9.86	25.79	18.28	32.05
14.87	24.65	15.70	8.65	4.42	17.20	8.53	0.45	0.95	4.44
7.45	5.82	45.20	2.70	10.04	15.70	32.20	12.43	36.75	32.50
16.87	3.78	0.56	33.67	9.67	25.50	33.06	7.56	2.63	45.80

The amount spent (in €) by the first 50 people going into a shop is shown in the table above. Questions 1 to 9 refer to this table.

1. Is this data discrete or continuous?
2. Draw up a grouped frequency table (with first group €0.01 – €10.00). You should have 6 groups.
3. Which is the modal group?
4. Enter the mid-values of each group and the frequencies onto your GDC. Calculate estimates of the mean and the standard deviation. (Why "estimates")?
5. Draw a bar chart to represent the data.
6. Complete a cumulative frequency table for the data, and hence draw a cumulative frequency graph.
7. From the cumulative frequency graph, write down the median, the lower quartile, the upper quartile and calculate the interquartile range.
8. Draw a box and whisker plot for the data.
9. What was the least amount that the people in the top ten percentiles spent?

LOGIC, SETS AND PROBABILITY

1. Draw a four row truth table and complete columns for the following propositions: $p \Rightarrow q; \neg p \wedge q; p \vee (p \wedge \neg q); \neg(p \veebar q)$.
2. Show that the proposition $p \Rightarrow (p \vee q)$ is a tautology.
3. On an eight row truth table, complete a column for the proposition $(\neg p \vee q) \Rightarrow r$.
4. "If it is hot then we will go to the beach." Write down the converse, the inverse and the contrapositive statements.
5. List the members of the following three sets:
   $A = \{x \mid x \text{ is even}, 2 \le x < 8\}; B = \{x \mid x \in Z, 1 \le x \le 5\}; A \cap B$
6. If $C = \{$all even numbers$\}$, and A and B are defined as in the previous question, which of the following are true: $A \subset C; C \subset A; A = C; B \cap C = \emptyset; A \cap C' = \emptyset$
7. Make copies of the Venn Diagram on the right and shade areas to represent: $P \cap Q; P' \cap Q; P' \cup Q'; (P' \cup Q)'$
8. Make a copy of the Venn Diagram and add another set R such that $R \subset P$ and $R \cap Q = \emptyset$.
9. Make a copy of the Venn Diagram and fill in the number of elements in each region such that: $n(U) = 30, n(P) = 18; n(Q) = 6; n(P \cup Q) = 21$.
10. Two dice are thrown. What is P(at least one shows a number greater than 1)?
11. I have 6 red socks and 4 green socks in a draw. I take 2 out at random. Draw a tree diagram to show the possible outcomes and find P(the two socks do not match).
12. A and B are two events such that $P(A) = 0.2$, $P(B) = 0.5$ and $P(A \cup B) = 0.55$. Use a Venn Diagram to find: $P(A \cap B); P(A' \cap B); P(A|B); P(B|A)$.
13. Two dice are rolled. Find the probability that they show different numbers given that the total is 8.
14. Given that $P(A \cup B) = 0.7$, $P(A) = 0.6$ and that A and B are independent events, find $P(B)$.

STATISTICAL APPLICATIONS

1. A normal distribution X has mean 56 and standard deviation 4. Find $P(X < 54)$, $P(X > 61)$, $P(53.5 < X < 60)$

2. In a normal distribution X, the values $X = a$ and $X = b$ are symmetrically placed either side of the mean. If $P(X < a) = 0.32$, find $P(a < X < b)$.
3. In a marathon race, the runners' times formed a normal distribution with $\mu = 205$ minutes, and $\sigma = 31$ minutes. What was the fastest time of the slowest 5% of runners, and the slowest time of the fastest 10% of runners?

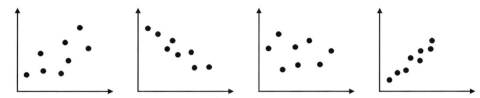

4. Match each of the scattergraphs above with one of the correlation coefficients -0.85, 0.0, 0.64, 0.92.
5. The table below shows the marks gained by 12 students in a chemistry assignment and a chemistry test.

Assignment (x)	5	9	7	11	20	4	6	17	12	10	15	16
Test (y)	6	8	9	13	20	9	8	17	14	8	17	18

Calculate the correlation coefficient, and find the regression line $y = ax + b$.
6. A thirteenth pupil missed the test because of illness. If she got 18 in the assignment, what mark should she be given in the test?
7. A random sample of 100 people were asked whether or not they drank "X-Lite". 62 said yes and 38 said no. After an advertising campaign another sample of 80 was asked the same question. 56 said yes and 24 said no. Draw up contingency tables for the observed and expected frequencies (Columns: Yes/No; Rows: Before/After campaign). Carry out a test at the 5% level to see if the advertising campaign has had an effect, given that the critical value = 3.841.

GEOMETRY AND TRIGONOMETRY
1. For the points A(2,3) and B(4,7), find: the midpoint; the distance AB; the gradient of AB; the equation of AB.
2. Repeat question 1 for the points A(-1,4) and B(-3,7).
3. Write down which pairs of lines are parallel and which are perpendicular:
   (a) $y = 2x + 5$; (b) $y + 2x = 1$; (c) $x = 4$; (d) $2y = x$; (e) $y - 2x + 3 = 0$; (f) $y = 3$.
4. Triangle PQR has a right angle at Q. PQ = 12cm, R = 23°. Calculate PR.
5. Triangle ABC has a right angle at A. AC = 2.4cm, AB = 1.8cm. Find C.
6. Solve the following triangles (the triangle in each case is ABC):
   BC = 6cm, C = 87°, A = 45°. Find AB.
   AB = 6cm, A = 87°, AC = 5.4cm. Find BC.
   AB = 6cm, BC = 5.4cm, CA = 3.5cm. Find B.
   AB = BC = 5.2cm. B = 34°. Find AC.
   AC = 6cm, C = 32°, A = 90°. Find AB.
   BC = 6cm, B = 62°, C = 71°. Find AC.
7. Find the area of the first and second triangles in question 6.
8. A line AB of length 60m is marked out on a river bank and the position of a tree C on the opposite bank is surveyed. It is found that CAB = 58° and CBA = 38°. Find CA and the width of the river.
9. Calculate the volume and surface area of a sealed cylinder with radius 3.5cm and height 8.3cm.
10. Calculate the volume and surface area of a sphere with diameter 8m.
11. Calculate the radius of a sphere with volume 128cm³.
12. Calculate the curved surface area of a cone with radius 5cm and height 8cm.
13. The square based pyramid on the right has AB = 10cm and
    AE = 12cm. Q is the midpoint of AB. Calculate the following:
    The lengths AC, AP, PE, QE.
    The angle between AE and the base.
    The angle between QE and the base.

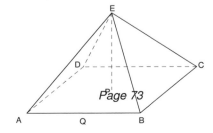

The angle between EB and EC.
The surface area of the pyramid (including the base).

MATHEMATICAL MODELS
1. What is the range of the function $f(x) = x^2 + 2$, $x \geq 1$?
2. Sketch the graph of $f(x) = \sqrt{(2 - x)}$, and hence write down the domain and range of the function.
3. Write down the gradients, x and y intercepts of the following straight line functions: $y = 2x - 5$; $3x - 2y = 8$; $x + y = 10$
4. Work out the equation of the line perpendicular to $y = 3x - 4$, which goes through the point $(1, 1)$.
5. Find the line of symmetry and the vertex of the graph of $y = x^2 - 2x + 6$.
6. For the graph of $y = 2(x - 3)(x + 1)$, write down the coordinates of the x intercepts, the y intercept and the vertex.
7. Some radioactive material decays such that its mass after t years is given by the formula $m = 12 \times 2^{-0.008t}$. What is its mass at $t = 0$ and after 100 years?
8. The graph with equation $y = 3^{2x} + k$ passes through the point $(1, 6)$. Find the value of k and find x when $y = -2$.

9. Use your GDC to solve the following equations: $x + 3 = \dfrac{2}{x}$; $x^3 = 2^x$.

10. Find the horizontal and vertical asymptotes on the graph of $y = \dfrac{2 + x}{3 - x}$.

11. Sketch the graph of $y = 0.5x^3 - \dfrac{2}{x}$, $-2 \leq x \leq 2$, $x \neq 0$. Mark any axis intercepts, and name the equation of the vertical asymptote.

INTRODUCTION TO DIFFERENTIAL CALCULUS
1. Differentiate the following functions:

$f(x) = 2x^3 - 3x^2 + 4x - 3$; $f(x) = x + \dfrac{6}{x}$; $f(x) = 4 - \dfrac{2}{x^3}$

2. What is the gradient of each of the curves in question 1 at the point where $x = 2$?
3. Find the equation of the tangent and the equation of the normal to $y = 3x^2 + 3$ at the point where $x = 1$.

4. Find the two points on the graph of $y = x - \dfrac{2}{x}$ where the gradient $= 3$.

5. By finding the values of $f(x)$ and $f'(x)$ at the points where $x = 2$ and $x = 3$ on the graph of $y = \frac{1}{2}x^2 - 2x + 1$, sketch the shape of the graph between the two points.
6. Use differentiation to find the turning point on the graph of $y = 6 - x + 3x^2$.
7. Use differentiation to find both turning points on the graph of $2x^3 - 24x$. Draw a sign diagram to decide which point is a maximum and which is a minimum.
8. Use your calculator to find all the turning points on the graph of $f(x) = x^2 \times 2^x$. State which are maxima and which are minima. Give answers to 3 significant figures where appropriate.
9. Find the gradient of the line joining the points $(2, 6)$ and $(3, 11)$ on the graph of $y = x^2 + 2$. Repeat for the line joining the points with x-coordinates 2 and 2.5, and then the line joining points with x-coordinates 2 and 2.1. What do your results suggest about the gradient of the tangent to the graph at the point where $x = 2$?

Answers to Practice Questions

NUMBER AND ALGEBRA
1. 0.269   **2.** 49.25875cm²   **3.** 0.0402%   **4.** 1.79×10^{-10} **5.** 16.11 m/s

6. 123, 7317 **7.** 120 **8.** 12582912, 6.87×10^{10} **9.** 0.7 **10.** $8982, $9006
11. $x = 1/3$, $y = 3$ **12.** $2x^2 + 5x + 2 = 0$, -0.5 or -2 **13.** €1.54, £0.65 **14.** $11.72
15. 684.8 crowns, 6720 crowns **16.** $3359.80, 3.44% **17.** 9 years **18.** €2258
19. $41.66 **20.** 11 years, 29 years

DESCRIPTIVE STATISTICS
1. Discrete. **2.**

0.01 – 10.00	10.01 – 20.00	20.01 – 30.00	30.01 – 40.00	40.01 – 50.00	50.01 – 60.00
20	14	4	9	2	1

3. 0.01 – 10.00 **4.** 17.4, 13.5; not using original data.
5.

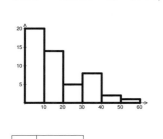

6.

€	≤10	≤ 20	≤ 30	≤ 40	≤ 50	≤60
c.f.	20	34	39	47	49	50

8.

7. $Q_1 = 6$, $Q_2 = 13$, $Q_3 = 26$, IQR = 20 **9.** €38

LOGIC, SETS AND PROBABILITY
1.

P	q	$p \Rightarrow q$	$\neg p \wedge q$	$p \vee (p \wedge \neg q)$	$\neg(p \veebar q)$
T	T	T	F	T	T
T	F	F	F	T	F
F	T	T	T	F	F
F	F	T	F	F	T

2.

P	q	$p \vee q$	$p \Rightarrow (p \vee q)$
T	T	T	T
T	F	T	T
F	T	T	T
F	F	F	T

Tautology

3.

p	q	r	$\neg p$	$\neg p \vee q$	$(\neg p \vee q) \Rightarrow r$
T	T	T	F	T	T
T	T	F	F	T	F
T	F	T	F	F	T
F	T	T	T	T	T
T	F	F	F	F	T
F	T	F	T	T	F
F	F	T	T	T	T
F	F	F	T	T	F

4. "If we go to the beach then it is hot."
"If it isn't hot then we won't go to the beach."
"If we don't go to the beach then it isn't hot."

5. {2,4, 6, 8}, {1,2,3,4,5}, {2, 4} **6.** T,F,F,F,T

7.

8.

9.

10. 35/36

11.

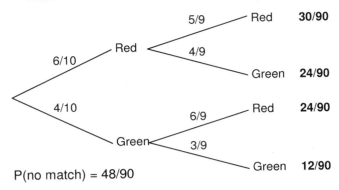

P(no match) = 48/90

12.

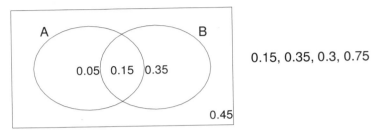

0.15, 0.35, 0.3, 0.75

13. 4/5   **14.** 0.25

STATISTICAL APPLICATIONS
1. 0.309, 0.106, 0.575   **2.** 0.36   **3.** 154 mins, 245 mins.   **4.** 0.64, -0.85, 0.0, 0.92
5. 0.94, $y = 0.88x + 2.58$ **6.** 18.4   **7.** $\chi^2 = 1.26$, campaign ineffective.

GEOMETRY AND TRIGONOMETRY
1. (3,5), 4.47, 2, $y = 2x - 1$.   **2.** (-2,5.5), 3.61, -1.5, $2y + 3x = 5$ **3.** ∥ a,e. ⊥ c,f; b,d.
4. 30.7   **5.** 36.9°   **6.** 8.47, 7.86, 35.3°, 3.04, 3.75, 7.24   **7.** 18.9, 16.2   **8.** 37.1, 31.5
9. 319.4cm^3, 259.5cm^2 **10.** 268.1m^3, 201.1m^2 **11.** 3.13cm   **12.** 148.2cm^2
13. 14.1cm, 7.07cm, 9.70cm, 10.9cm; 53.9°; 62.7°; 49.2°; 318cm^2

MATHEMATICAL MODELS
1. $f(x) \geq 3$ **2.** $x \leq 2$, $f(x) \geq 0$ **3.** 2, 2.5, -5; 1.5,8/3, -4; -1, 10, 10   **4.** $x + 3y = 4$
5. $x = 1$, (1,5)   **6.** (3,0), (-1,0); (0,-6); (1,-8)   **7.** 12, 6.89   **8.** -3, 0
9. 0.562 and -3.56, 1.373   **10.** $y = -1$, $x = 3$ **11.**

INTRODUCTION TO DIFFERENTIAL CALCULUS
1. $6x^2 - 6x + 4$, $1 - \dfrac{6}{x^2}$, $\dfrac{6}{x^4}$.   **2.** 16, -0.5, 0.375   **3.** $y = 6x$, $x + 6y = 37$ **4.** (1,-1), (-1,1)

5. $f(x) = -1$ and -0.5, $f'(x) = 0$ and 1   **6.** $\left(\frac{1}{6}, 5\frac{11}{12}\right)$ **7.** (2,-32) min, (-2,32) max

8. (-2.89, 1.13) max, (0,0) min   **9.** 5, 4.5, 4.1; Tending towards 4.

Version 3.31